Miss Gladys *and the* Pit Bull Barracuda

Dave Kilbourne

FLYING PIG PRESS

Published by Flying Pig Press
2380 Alamo Avenue
Chico, California 95926

ISBN: 978-0-9855316-0-7

Library of Congress Card Number: 2012938890
Printed in the United States of America

DEDICATION

THIS BOOK IS DEDICATED TO:

Savannah A. Kilbourne,
The Finest Daughter In All The Land

My Brother, Dixon Roy Kilbourne,
A Christian Gentleman and Great American

My Unique Parents,
The Sainted Gladys Mae Kilbourne
and
The Highly Eccentric Harry Kenneth Kilbourne

ACKNOWLEDGEMENTS

A long list of people deserve thanks for their help and encouragement in making this book happen. However, that list must begin with **Ruth Younger** and **Connie Ballou**, two special friends and consummate wordsmiths who caused this book to come together with proper words and excellent appearance.

Ruth Younger: Ruth is a longtime friend and the best editor ever. Ruth *got it* from the beginning and was able to work very effectively with my eccentric, idiomatic writing style. Ruth provided valuable suggestions on how to make numerous stories even better with just a slight adjustment here and there. For example, in the story *Davie's Gone Flying with Santa,* Ruth is responsible for providing the Baby Jesus with a snug little manger fashioned from an old mullet crate.

When I realized that I needed an editor, I called the best first. I'm grateful she was home that afternoon. Here's to you Ruth. Meet me in the Pub, back by the pizza oven. The beer's on me!

Connie Ballou: The Proprietor of Chico's very successful Back Alley Graphics has proven to be the essence of patience and understanding. Connie provided excellent help with the book design as well as with the dreaded PDF Print Ready File. She has been in constant danger of getting the Howling Skitters if she had to make one more **** *formatting* change.

Connie displayed a degree of patience and understanding far beyond the call of duty. Each time I assured her that there would be no further changes, I was soon forced to call her and sadly admit that, yes, there would be a *few* more *minor* changes before we could consider ourselves done with the book formatting and design work.

Several times these *few minor changes* involved completely reformatting the entire book. This could be very exciting for her and on the third reformat she started vibration all over and her eyes rolled so far back into her head ... but she got it done and when last seen was still smiling grimly.

Barbara O. Geshekter: Author of *Words to That Effect* and my official personal writing muse. The name *Barbara* is Latin for one of the nine mythical goddess muses that preside over literature and the arts. She has been a strong source of literary inspiration and has offered spirited encouragement from the beginning.

A select few know that I wrote several of the stories in this book simply for her own personal enjoyment. She gave me lots of creative ideas while she was in beer training and always waited patiently for the next story.

Savannah A. Kilbourne: The finest daughter in all the land! She has faithfully read all of my stories first, before anyone else, even before my good friend and boon companion Barbara Geshekter. Savannah is more than willing to add her constructive criticism and useful suggestions. Several of her useful suggestions began with, "Daddy you should just start this one all over again." Additional encouragement came in the form of her evaluation of my traditional Rice Orgy Parisienne recipe: "This stuff is way flushable." See *The Discovery of Rice Orgy Parisienne* and decide for yourself.

The *late* Karen Potter: Not to worry. The worthy Karen is still fully alive and as vivacious as ever … *but she is always late!* She has a bumper sticker on her car, which I gave her (the sticker, not the car) that reads, *On time is when I get there.* Another sticker I awarded her bumper is *This is the earliest I've ever been late!* If truth were told, she is *always late but worth the wait*…whoa….that's another good one!

I've waited patiently for her for many years and it has always been worth the effort. Karen brings it! Several of the stories in this book were written with herself in mind.

Karen is actually a lovely highly evolved woman, longtime friend and excellent companion. She has proven to be a valuable advisor on anything having to do with *social situations* and I often go to her to ask her well-thought-out advice on some mischief or other Savannah has gotten into or caused to happen. Karen's evaluation of my writing was always the same, "Very funny Dave, very funny."

Furthermore, I want to give a shout out and a air high five to Karen as Publisher of *The Synthesis,* a highly informative weekly newspaper of wide circulation and excellent reputation that focuses on Chico's upbeat pop culture scene. Much respect!

Beta Readers: Richard Parker, Rob Burton, and Steve and Mary Bohnemeyer served as initial readers as the original manuscript was being developed. While their valuable assistance and advice could be bought for the price of a few pints of Sierra Nevada's finest, the value of their involvement was priceless and well beyond my budget.

The Sierra Nevada Ownership and Management Team: Thanks for your excellent hospitality throughout the years as well as during the historic Beer Camp No. 69 adventure and beyond.

■ *His Eminence,* **Ken Grossman:** Pope of The Church of the Holy Nectar and Inventor of Chico's world-famous Sierra Nevada Pale Ale.

■ *His Beatific Presence,* **Steve Dresler:** High Priest and Master Brewer of the Holy Sacrament.

■ *Father* **Al Spinelli:** Overseer General of The Church of the Holy Nectar.

■ *Father* **Bill Manley:** Minister of Good Will of the Brew Church.

■ *Brother* **Terence Sullivan:** Counselor of the Holy Beer Encampment.

The Sierra Nevada Pub Crew: A round of applause for all their goodwill and generosity while providing me with a little space back by the pizza oven to call my own as I wrote this book.

All of these gentles have a special place in my heart for upon my arrival for worship each Thursday evening, just before vespers, they faithfully stand ready with my holy vessel. Verily, this sanctified vessel is brought forth from within the holy goblet sanctuary with the least amount of delay. Additionally, these faithful gentles generously bring forth small amounts of any nectar newly released since my previous visit. Among these worthies are Sister **Mary Barrow,** Sister **Ash Candler,** Brother **Corey Jack,** Sister **Kristen Forte,** Sister **Jessica Sid** and Brother **Casey Sylvester,** as well as others too numerous to name.

Tammi of Nazareth: These heartfelt acknowledgements would not be complete without a raising of the sanctified vessel to Tammi of Nazareth. A holy figure of ginormous biblical presence and comportment, Tammi and I encountered one another at The Church of the Holy Nectar one star-crossed evening just after Vespers. She had traveled from her villa on the Sea of Galilee to visit friends in Chico for the summer. Like her better-known older brother, Tammi had powers that went beyond the understanding of mere mortals! She possessed a heavenly radiance of enormous proportions. Google *Tammi of Nazareth* and behold ....

Noble Readers: And last, my thanks and appreciation to all of you gentles who read for pleasure. I hope you experienced a few smiles along your way through these pages.

 I *especially* want to thank any of you worthies who have actually paid for this book as the earnings from this project go towards my daughter Savannah's medical fund ... and if I can sell enough of these books, she can have that operation to replace that little leg. Then she can run and jump and play with all the other children. Call for further details on this special offer.

CONTENTS

PROLOGUE

Why I Had to Write This Book

FOR ALL OF THE YEAR 2011, I had the pleasure of being a guest columnist for the *Chico Enterprise-Record*, a daily of some excellent quality and reputation. During those months, I was paid a modest stipend for writing humor columns, a fact that changed my status from amateur to professional writer.

In the past, other guest columnists traditionally wrote stories about uplifting life experiences or well thought-out essays concerning their beliefs, aspirations and/or favorite pets. However, my stories were characterized by humor based on my lifelong study of human nature. Those humans are very funny, and among the funniest are members of my immediate family, especially my father, a character who gives new meaning to the phrase *profoundly eccentric*. He was a self-certified soothsayer.

A little background. My father strongly believed that the great pyramids of ancient Egypt were built by a superior cosmic civilization rather than by the ancient Egyptians themselves. He further believed that these benevolent space engineers might have originally been from the lost island of Atlantis. My father had theories! He felt that the ancient Egyptian simply didn't have the technology to design and construct these timeless monuments, although he admitted they might have invented the refreshing beverage commonly referred to as beer. You just can't make this kind of stuff up! If you like the sound of that little story, turn immediately to *Growing Up as the Son of a Soothsayer*. There will be no additional charge.

Previous to becoming a newspaper columnist and writer of humorous tales, I had made a fairly good living as a writer of long-winded and excruciatingly boring reports, manuals, proposals, and guidebooks. Most had to do with the general subject of downtown revitalization and economic development. Not very entertaining and certainly not exciting unless you were a downtown business or property owner.

For example, my solution for chronic insomnia was entitled *Guidelines for Forming a Downtown Business Improvement District Under California Senate Bill 1424: An Instruction Manual.* Merely place this book under your pillow or even anywhere within your bedroom and you will enjoy a deep slumber within sixty seconds. Guaranteed or your money back. Call us in the morning.

After twenty years of writing mind-deadening economic development publications, I had nowhere to go but up regarding the entertainment value of any future writing. Decide for yourself which of these two titles is more provocative and interesting: *A Guidebook for Public Signage Modification* ... or ... *The All New Porkgasmic Belly Rotator, A Modern Miracle!* You be the judge.

During my year as a newspaper columnist, I enjoyed some modest encouragement and support. More than once (actually twice!) friends and admirers suggested that I consider publishing my newspaper columns as well as some of those other stories I had been entertaining folks with over the years. I suggested reissuing the dramatic and exciting *Guidelines for Forming a Downtown Business Improvement District Under California Senate Bill 1424.* I was sternly discouraged.

One of my most faithful supporters, the lovely Barbara Geshekter (herself an author of some acclaim), encouraged me to organize and compile this book. Therefore, if you don't like it, or if you have read it and now want your money back, please contact Ms. Geshekter.

I also enjoyed a supportive yet somewhat ambivalent relationship with Mr. David Little, the highly esteemed Editor of the *Chico Enterprise-Record.* I quickly learned that writing a newspaper column had several drawbacks that could be summarized in one word: RULES.

I also discovered that Editors enjoy having the final say. While Editor Little was always very encouraging, at the same time he also persisted in doing his job, which included limiting my stories to a mere 700 words! I suppose I shouldn't complain since the limit was actually roughly 600 words; however, some of his editing seemed brutal. For example, I wrote this perfectly good sentence: *And then Uncle Bubba developed the electronified pork pulling machine, which was truly a modern miracle.* Sounds about right, doesn't it? Now, here is the edited sentence: *The pork machine was a modern miracle.* He performed that word amputation without even offering anesthesia! A Sierra Nevada Torpedo IPA would have been welcome.

Additionally, Editor Little was a punctuation Nazi when it came to using exclamation points! When editing my first column, he revealed himself to be a founding member of the Anti-Exclamation League! I had used a mere three exclamation points, which is minimal for me because I can be, how do they say … excitable! I was astounded when Editor Little called to say that I would be limited to one exclamation point for the entire year! This seemed both unreasonable and un-American, but he was the boss … unless I wrote my own book. Then I could use up the world's supply of those little (pun intended!) punctuation marks, and no one would be counting! Editor Little would no doubt be delighted to see them all used up and off the face of the English language. And that, worthy reader, is why I had to write this book.

Another diabolic habit of his was adjusting my column title after I had spent entire minutes getting it just right. For example (again, you be the judge!), I submitted my inaugural column with this excellent title: *A Short History of the Friday Evening Naked Gentlemen's Billiards Society, LLC, Est. 1988.* This says it all to me, short and to the point yet provocative. In response, he immediately, and without warning, changed it to *Pool Parties a Reliable Diversion.* What?? Gadzooks! This sounds like an activity occurring in close proximity to a swimming pool, which conveyed nothing about the amusing history of my gentle friends and myself enjoying a Friday evening game of billiards while drinking a pint or two of Sierra Nevada's finest. I didn't know about this title change business until I picked up the paper in great anticipation of seeing my words in print. I skipped right past my column because the title was so not mine. The horror!

So in retrospect, these onerous rules and regulations, plus a little encouragement from friends and lots of tough love from David Little (who is actually very charming and a prince of a fellow) drove me to write my own book. So, Mr. Editor-in-Chief, these exclamations are for you!!!

Another refreshing and healthful factor came into play as I diddled around deciding whether I had enough words within me to write three dozen stories and then publish them for you to enjoy, noble reader. That factor was my long-term excellent association with Chico's Sierra Nevada Brewing Company, the finest brewery in all the land! While I have no ownership or employee connection, I have invested considerable time and money in the Sierra Nevada Pub, which I know as *The Church of the Holy Nectar* (see related story inside this book). I wrote a majority of the stories in this collection while worshipping inside *The Church of the Holy Nectar.* Over the period of a year, give or take a pint or two, I spent a lot of creative time there. During this period my address was simply *Dave, Sierra Nevada Taproom, back by the pizza oven.* I still occasionally get mail delivered there. Maybe that's not such a good sign. Do you get your mail delivered to a tavern?

Also, most stories in this collection were first told to friends while sharing a pleasant hour at the pub. The best of the litter were referred to as *second beer stories,* as I insisted on finishing my first pint while they impatiently waited before I'd launch into that week's special tale. I would savor the last tiny sips of that first pint while rolling my eyes and smacking my lips deliciously in order to draw out the suspense. This facetious habit did not increase my popularity during my weekly holding forth at the Taproom. Sorry, there are no third beer stories because telling those would require that I take the back way home and I like to go home the front way.

So gentle readers, I hope you enjoy reading these amazing (mostly) true stories of human adventure as much as I enjoyed telling them. You have my address, *Sierra Nevada Brewery, back by the pizza oven,* if you want to get in touch. Cheers!

Dave Kilbourne, L.W.S., E.T.C.
—Licensed Word Smith—

Writer of Words
Specializing in English Language Words
Synonyms, Antonyms, Homonyms & Idioms
Metaphors, Analogies & Similes
Lavish use of Vowels & Consonants

—

Partial Listing of Services Provided:
Humorous Wedding Toasts & Obituaries
Written Statements of All Kinds for All Purposes
Fictionalized Accounting of Supposedly True Events
Columnist, Humorist, Satirist, & Ironist
Personal Memoirs of Little Consequence
Oxymorons for All Occasions
Quotes, Quips, Witticisms
Witty Repartee & Insults
Criticisms, Critiques & Other Self-Serving Verbosity
Unsolicited Opinions Ad Nauseam
Tall Tales & Short Stories
Book Reports & Homework Assignments
Miscellaneous Instructions for Assembly
Advice & Personal Servicing of the Lovelorn
Granting of Poetic License
Microbrew Journalism, Recipes & Tasting Reviews
Pharmaceutical Prescriptions

—

campkilbrn@aol.com
530-345-0900 (o)
530-680-5776 (m)
2380 Alamo Avenue, back by the pizza oven
Chico, CA. 95926
www.flyingpigpress.net

My official all purpose business card … clip out and laminate.

PART ONE

TALES OF THE CAROLINA
LOW COUNTRY

Headquarters of Georgetown County Hags and Plat-Eyes when they are not away from home terrorizing the locals who have not had the foresight to apply Plat-Eye Blue paint to their doors and windows. Note lack of paint around doors and windows.

Growing Up with Spiritual Terrorists in the Carolina Low Country

BEWARE OF HAGS AND PLAT-EYES in the Carolina Low Country! My brother, Dixon Roy Kilbourne, a Great American, and I spent our idyllic childhood growing up on Pawleys Island, a small beach community deep in the swampy low country of beautiful Georgetown County. At that time, Pawleys Island was only slightly connected to the state of South Carolina by a rickety old causeway.

There couldn't have been a better *home place* to grow and flourish in than the fertile environment of salt air and sunshine, except for one small drawback: the great preponderance of Hags and Plat-Eyes. Any woman could be a Hag. Your wife could be a Hag. So could your mother-in-law. In the daylight Hags are *ordinary* females, if such a creature exists. It is at night that they become ticklish creatures of diabolic torment, much like an old girl I once went out with. These creatures have been referred to as *The Terrible Awful* by those who have personally suffered through their attentions.

Your Plat-Eyes, on the other hand, are spirits that can take the form of other animals or objects. Plat-Eyes have two front teeth, but no back teeth. When they are not disguised as other creatures, such as your common swamp troll, Plat-Eyes have one big eye, like a grits plate; hence the name Plat-Eye. A medium-sized Plat-Eye can wreak havoc in your hog pen and chicken coop, if access is carelessly allowed. Ham and eggs is their meal of choice for a midnight snack. They like their food very rare.

On idyllic Pawleys Island, everything changes when the sunshine turns to dusk and the giant live oaks cast deep shadows with their beards of Spanish moss, for it is during this time that the spirits come out on the hunt to terrorize small boys and puppies. For some spiritual reason they don't bother with girls or kittens.

Your typical Hag comes while you are sleeping, slipping into your house through a keyhole, an open window or even an unsecured pet door. Once inside, the hag will *ride* you throughout the long night while tickling you all over with a hoot owl feather. Victims ridden by a fully-grown swamp hag wake up feeling disoriented and exhausted from the night sweats and thoroughly weak in the knees.

In response to this threat, natives of the Low Country have come up with a variety of remedies to prevent a late-night visitation from your occasional Hag or Plat-Eye. You can keep them from entering your house by painting the windows and doorframes a certain bright blue. This color is often referred to as *Plat-Eye Blue* at the local paint store, as in, "Give me two gallons of your most powerful Plat-Eye Blue, and I need it before sundown!"

I have read that other effective defenses include scattering a cupful of long grain rice on the floor near your doors and windows. A Hag will stop and pick up every one of those grains before continuing into the house. Propping a broom upside down next to your door also works. The Hag will count every straw in that broom before continuing into your bedroom.

Another effective way to slow the Plat-Eye down is through the use of the *Plat-Eye Early Warning System* (PEEWS). My elder brother and I developed this system ourselves and it always worked for us. Use these easy to follow directions: 1) Get yourself a medium-size brownish dog full of fleas. 2) At night place dog upon your chest up near the neck area. The Plat-Eye will have to stop and count all the fleas on the PEEWS before continuing on to terrorize the intended victim. It is thought that your Hags and your Plat-Eyes suffer from Obsessive-Compulsive Disorder.

A strategy planning session during the original development of the "Plat Eye Early Warning System" (PEEWS). Elder brother is on the right. On the left is a small boy who used to hang around whenever it came on close to lunchtime. We think his name was Lamar something something. Mr. Chumley can be seen in dog costume.

According to a well-informed Hag scholar in the North Georgia Mountains, there is one last measure of defense you can use to protect yourself even as a Hag is about to ride you. You can put a flour sifter with a fork underneath it directly over your face. You will probably wake up when the hag starts whispering as she counts all the holes in the sifter. Then you can pull the flour sifter off your face and quickly pin the Hag inside it with the fork. If you can just keep the Hag pinned until sunrise, it will be too late for her to return to her skin. After that you're on your own. Unfortunately, the Hag will be somewhat moody.

So, you ask, how does one protect oneself from all these Hags and Plat-Eyes that abound in the Carolina Low Country? It is simple, really. You just get a *conjure doctor* to whip you up a largish Boo-Daddy (pat. pend.), which is made from a mixture of marsh mud, Spanish moss, saltwater, and something very similar to Sierra Nevada's finest Bigfoot Ale. A fully-grown Boo-Daddy is the natural enemy of your Hags and Plat-Eyes.

Once formed by the *conjure doctor,* the Boo-Daddy is incubated inside a marsh oyster. Boo-Daddies renew their power every month, under the full moon, by going back to drink the ale-like nectar from the oysters. Boo-Daddies have large heads, big teeth and shapeless bodies, much like that old gal I once went out with.

Note: If the reader would like to learn more about Low Country Hags and Plat-Eyes, consider *Ghosts of Georgetown* and *More Ghosts of Georgetown* by the very well-informed Elizabeth Robertson Huntsinger. I found these excellent books at the world famous *Pawleys Island Hammock Shop.* If you go there, ask for Darlene. She is a very delightful and gracious young Southern Belle who will see that you are given a sample of delicious fudge. There will be no charge.

Davie's Gone Flying with Santa, A True Christmas Story

ONCE UPON A TIME, a long time ago, I went flying with Santa Claus. His actual full name was *Smiling Jack Malloy and His Aerial Stunt Circus.* My mother said Smiling Jack Malloy was not fully civilized and did not have good mental hygiene.

At the time, my father, the storied Harry Kenneth Kilbourne, was Manager of the Chamber of Commerce in Georgetown, South Carolina, where one of his primary job responsibilities was dreaming up and facilitating most of the *special events,* such as parades and beauty contests that occurred on the annual civic calendar. There was a special place in his heart for beauty contests.

He enjoyed this part of his job and was not above suggesting that there be no less than four beauty contests each year, one for each season. There was a *Miss Beachcomber,* a *Miss Pulled Pork,* a *Miss Cotton Festival,* and his favorite, a *Miss Shrimp and Grits* contest, which was tied in closely with the shrimp boaters' association. This motley crew was a lively lot; they were dedicated believers in the many benefits of consuming robust drink, much similar to Sierra Nevada Brewing Company's delicious Torpedo Ale, which proudly tops out at a hearty 7.2 ABV.

Another special event, which he enjoyed, was the planning and implementing of the annual Christmas parade. While he was a very creative person, some said dangerously so, the yearly challenge of coming up with a new and different way for Santa to arrive at the Christmas Parade could be daunting. One year Santa arrived on a fire engine, and once he was brought in on a shrimp boat. Another Christmas he arrived riding upon a scrofulous rental camel with the chronic mange that was pulling a little nativity cart with the Baby Jesus fast asleep in a manger that was fashioned from an old mullet box.

After four or five years of dreaming up new and creative ways for Santa to arrive and lead the Christmas parade, my father admitted that he was stumped. It was at this point that he conceived one of his most dangerous *special events*. He decided, in an instant of rare clarity, that Santa would arrive in an aeroplane. He convinced one of his chronic golfing/beer drinking buddies, Smiling Jack Malloy, who had a dilapidated 1927 open cockpit Cessna, with which he terrorized the community with flying tricks anytime he was aloft, to participate in the new Santa arrival stunt. The flying Santa would need an elf to serve as assistant. My father took me aside to explain that the elf should be about ten years old, which I realized with great trepidation, was my exact age.

One problem was that I had never flown before and felt strongly that I wanted to maintain that status forever. Additionally, I was very afraid of heights as well as of being confined in a small space. Most of all, I was deathly afraid of *Smiling Jack Malloy* the stunt pilot, who had very poor, possibly disabling, mental hygiene. My concerns were not addressed.

The plan was for the aeroplane to land in a grits field near downtown and then taxi down Front Street to the beginning of the parade route. Smiling Jack Malloy, dressed in a full Santa costume, would then dismount and hand out small gifts to the children. At this point, if I survived, my job would be over and I would be allowed to go run and jump and play with all the other regular children, although I would still have my elf costume on.

My mother had learned long ago to closely monitor my father's *creative* plans and activities due to several previous death-defying events that included myself, the youngest and most vulnerable son. As the parade was forming up and the kids were all competing for the best space right at the curb, my mother asked my father if he had seen me recently. He responded hesitantly, "Well, actually Davie's gone flying with Santa, but he'll be back soon. Not to worry." My mother gave forth with a panicked look and said sternly, "Well, he had better come back all in one piece!"

Meanwhile, at the airport we were running late due to Smiling Jack Malloy not being able to get the Cessna started until he sprayed a large dose of pure ethanol alcohol directly into the carburetor. This caused a small fire and a lot of black smoke. After Smiling Jack extinguished the fire, he lifted me up and strapped me into the back seat of the decrepit old aeroplane. He furnished me with a frayed old leather flying helmet and a set of WWI flying goggles with one lens missing. He said to just keep that eye closed. He had one reluctant elf on his hands.

My role in the Santa-arrives-by-airplane stunt would be to go aloft with Smiling Jack Malloy, the Stunt Pilot, who had questionable mental health, and assist him with his Flying Stunt Circus activities. Because his small aeroplane was an open cockpit model, that would facilitate my casting little candy canes down upon the heads of innocent spectators lining the parade route below. As we taxied down the little dirt runway, and as I prepared to carry out my assigned duties, I was pleased to note that the little candy canes were not individually wrapped. At this point I admit, freely and without shame that, as a sort of personal touch, I endeavored to lick each and every individual candy cane before casting it down upon the head of some unsuspecting parade watcher.

I have recently learned that as a result of my wanton licking of each and every candy cane, there is now some sort of ridiculous law that requires food items be individually wrapped before distribution to the consumer. I feel proud that this requirement may be due to my personal actions during that distressing day. In my own defense, let it be explained that I required an extra sugar intake in order to cope with the extraordinary stressors and tensions placed upon my ten-year-old self that special day during the Christmas season in Georgetown County, South Carolina.

Once aloft and over the downtown area, we could see that the parade with its bands and local dignitaries, and the float upon which *Miss Pulled Pork* was riding, was getting underway. Smiling Jack The Stunt Pilot said, "Don't worry, we'll catch up quick once we get rid of the candy!" He then said to hold on tight to the open cardboard box containing one thousand little candy canes and then turned the dilapidated aeroplane exactly upside down. The hailstorm of candy canes cascaded from the plane and then the cardboard box followed behind because I had wisely opted to hold on to the aeroplane rather than on to the box.

When we landed in the grits field, I had several pre-licked candy canes stuck to my elf costume and my hair had turned completely white, which it still is to this day.

In this historic photograph, my sainted mother, Gladys Mae Kilbourne, known to all as Miss Gladys, *innocently prepares to catch a Pit Bull Barracuda strictly by accident while her able fishing assistant, yours truly, sits idly by offering no assistance.*

Miss Gladys and the Pit Bull Barracuda

MY MOTHER HAD DEEP-SEATED ISSUES WITH FISH. Once upon a time, many years ago, my father, who was Manager of the Georgetown County Chamber of Commerce at the time, was able to convince my Sainted Mother, Gladys Mae Kilbourne, that it would be in the best interest of the Chamber if she participated in the Annual Fishing Rodeo. She never completely recovered from that traumatic experience. This account concerns that troubling time.

My mother had strong opinions about those who went out to sea in pursuit of game fish. She said they were motivated by an overload of testosterone and strong drink. She further pointed out that the fish they caught seldom ended up on the family dinner table, but rather ended up being stuffed by some taxidermist, who was probably himself laboring under the influence of strong drink. Then the dead fish was hung on a trophy wall where it spent its time collecting dust, as was the case of the unfortunate swordfish that hung directly above her desk at the offices of the Georgetown County Chamber of Commerce.

During this time, my mother was the secretary down at the Chamber, which was under the uncertain management of my highly eccentric father, Harry Kenneth Kilbourne. My father felt that his main responsibility to the Chamber was to plan no less than four (4) beauty *pageant*s each year, as well as come up with a new and creative way to bring Santa Claus into town for the annual Christmas Parade. Once he brought Santa into the downtown area riding upon a scrofulous rental camel, with the chronic mange, that was pulling a little nativity cart with the Baby Jesus in it, fast asleep in his little manger. Another time he had Santa brought in on an aeroplane flown by the infamous Smiling Jack Malloy, the Stunt Pilot, who suffered from poor mental health. But that is another story.

My father was a sporting man and played a lot of golf during the week. He claimed it was associated with his public relations work. When I casually mentioned one day that he must have a second office out at the golf course, he responded sternly that the work he accomplished while golfing was very important and was not to be taken lightly. He said that he *networked* and did serious *planning activities* while on the golf course with his *business associates*. He greatly enjoyed eighteen holes of golf with his Chamber buddies and could be found out there on the local course any time he could think of a reasonable excuse to leave the day-to-day Chamber business in the capable hands of my mother.

When my father was first hired as Chamber Manager, he asked if there might also be a place for my mother since they worked as sort of a team. He explained that he would apply his creative thinking and fertile imagination to the development of a calendar of annual civic events and activities and she would be responsible for the *day to day* office management activities. As a result of his persuasive ways, my mother was indeed hired to serve as sort of a second-in-command and was given the title of Office Manager. He was the Chamber Manager and she was the Office Manager. Everyone referred to her as "Miss Gladys down at the Chamber." Everyone referred to him as "That golfer guy who plans all the festivals and parades and gets his picture in the *Georgetown Times* a lot."

One of my father's favorite activities was being the main planner and person in charge of the Annual Georgetown Fishing Rodeo. This event was another of the Chamber of Commerce's many original and creative civic events, which they sponsored as a means of promoting the benefits and virtues of Georgetown within the three-county region and beyond. It seemed to work, as hoards of Georgetown County citizens continually flocked into the traditional downtown area to view and participate in such unique events as the *Miss Shrimp and Grits Festival,* the *Cotton*

Festival, and the unforgettable *Miss Pulled Pork Festival.* Folks came from far and wide. They came from as wide and far away as Charleston, Columbia, and Savannah to see what was going on in downtown Georgetown. I recall that seasonal parades with beauty queens seemed to be a main theme. My father liked his beauty contests and often appointed his golfing and fishing cronies, as well as someone from the *Times,* preferably the Editor, to serve as judges.

Several other of my father's special events and activities were also quite popular and enjoyed a loyal support base. Events such as the Annual Chamber Golf Tournament and the Georgetown Fishing Rodeo were examples of highly successful events he developed while dreaming up new mischief out on the golf course. He once said that golf *stimulated his creative imagination.*

I clearly recall the year the Chamber decided to invite the women of the community to participate in the Annual Fishing Rodeo, which was traditionally an all-male competition. After several weeks of getting the word out about this rare opportunity, and still not hearing from even one *fisherwoman,* my father decided that my mother should sign up to participate in the rodeo. He planned to parlay this into a newsworthy event, which would then become a photo opportunity to be printed in the *Georgetown Times.* His thinking was that other ladies in the community would see the newspaper item and be encouraged to sign up. My mother was popular with the local golfing and fishing widows, and was known to be the more well-grounded member of the two-person Chamber management team.

Unfortunately, Miss Gladys had a thing about fish, and didn't like to associate with them. She would eat a fish, which she referred to as *the bounty of the sea,* but she refused to touch the outsides of any fish, which she described as *slimy and scaly.* My father admitted that, yes, there was a certain scaliness to them, since they were covered with scales from stem to stern. However, he explained, they were quite sanitary, and came out of the ocean all clean, which was a condition they achieve from swimming in the water all their lives.

My mother did not want to have any part in the fishing rodeo, which she described as *another one of Ken's crazy ideas*. He carefully explained the importance of her setting an example for the other women in the community, and even went so far as to suggest that this might be part of her duty as a Chamber employee. My father was a fast-talking carpetbagger and my mother was not immune to his charms, which he would dial up to a ferocious level when he really wanted something to go his way. She often said that my father was *only partly civilized and could be a vexation*.

After much more cajoling and a lot of eye-rolling on my father's part, my mother finally agreed to participate in the Georgetown Fishing Rodeo, but only under certain very strict guidelines. She should not have to actually catch any fish, and she should certainly not have to touch a fish, under any circumstances. As was mentioned earlier, she has issues with fish, much like my elder brother. He, however, had to be restrained with the use of a stout chain harness whenever he was allowed to go down to the fish docks. He required someone to closely monitor his behavior whenever he was around live fish, especially the mullet fish, so I always had to go along and *keep an eye on him*. But that's another story, and it's better not to go into any further details about his unfortunate condition, which has been thoroughly studied by the College of Charleston Department of Mental Hygiene.

Anyway, during the brief time that my mother would be required to actually drop a line in the water, my official job would be to assist her and see that her cast got away from the boat and out into the ocean. I was also to stand by at all times just in case some ignorant fish with a death wish tried to get caught by her. My mother, who didn't understand the finer principles of fishing, didn't feel it was necessarily a good thing to get a fish *stuck* and flopping around on the end of your line.

The day of the Annual Georgetown Fishing Derby arrived bright and early with a balmy tropical breeze blowing across a sunny, flat ocean surface. We put out to sea aboard the fancy motor vessel, *Miss Demeanor,* formerly *The Fish Killer,* which belonged to Captain Sammy Crayton, whom we later discovered was a first cousin of the infamous Smiling Jack Malloy, the Stunt Pilot. Captain Crayton had a two-boat fleet of fishing vessels. The other boat was named *Miss Behavior.*

My mother and I had been enjoying the mellow sun and chatting about everything but fishing when all of a sudden, something big grabbed her bait. She grew sore afraid, much similar to the time Grandma Kilbourne got her bib overalls caught in the wringer of the washing machine and almost strangulated herself. But that's another story. With great trepidation, my mother wanted to know if there was a fish on her line. "Oh, that's probably a friendly little amberjack just tasting your delicious calamari," I said soothingly.

However, I had actually seen the needle-nose snout just beneath the surface, as it maliciously smiled, displaying rows of razor-sharp teeth. I knew, with a deep sense of unease, that it was undoubtedly the dreaded Pit Bull Barracuda that had eaten her squid. This fish, one of the most feared of all ocean-dwelling piscatores, had thoughtlessly chosen to hook itself to my non-fishing mother's fishing line. The Pit Bull Barracuda takes the job of feeding itself very seriously and is not to be trifled with. Great White Sharks have been known to run themselves aground on the nearest beach to escape a small school of your juvenile Pit Bull Barracudas.

My mother had big fish trouble on the end of her line. What to do? It seemed unfair that I had to face these decisions on my own. However, even at my tender age of ten years, I was an old soul whose youth had been carelessly spent on older women and strong drink. Orange Crush was my preferred beverage at the time. Furthermore, I was currently *involved* with Marlene Updagrove, a mature woman of twelve. She'd told me we were engaged. I was beginning to feel the weight of my years.

My father was missing in action as he was back on the docks *officiating* the rodeo by overseeing the weighing in of the fish as they were brought off the boats. On our boat, Monsignor Billy Jack, Capt. Crayton's First Mate, was occupied with an attractive young widow lady who had gotten her hook snarled with the back side of her flimsy little fishing shorts. Meanwhile, the Pit Bull Barracuda was making a dash for freedom and the reel on my mother's light-weight little fishing rod was starting to heat up and put out steam.

Against my better judgment, I went to the stern of the boat and located my elder brother, Dixon Roy Kilbourne, a robust youth of twelve years, who much later evolved into a Great American and Christian Gentleman. I grabbed him by his overalls bib and hauled him back up to the forepeak of *Miss Demeanor* where I had strapped our mother securely to the chain locker. She only weighed one hundred pounds, and I didn't want her getting dragged overboard. When we got back to her, she was looking entirely overwhelmed by the idea of actually catching a live fish. It was obvious that the Pit Bull Barracuda at the other end of the line was definitely alive and intending to stay that way. He was whipping out a lot of light line, perhaps chasing a great white shark out of his territorial feeding ground.

Sadly, as was mentioned earlier, my brother Dickie had his own personal issues with fish, especially live ones, and had to be carefully watched at all times. If truth were told, several times in the recent past the SPCA had to be called as a result of his *acting out behavior* with any number of fresh mullet. The nice SPCA folks always chuckled and said that he *was a caution* as they took him back home in their little truck with the sturdy box on the back. Dickie always liked to ride in the back with the fish when they escorted him home. Everyone agreed that my brother truly loved his fresh mullet.

Meanwhile, back aboard *Miss Demeanor,* after a great deal of shouting and shoving with everyone trying to get involved in the action, we were finally able to play out and reel in the barracuda enough times to finally exhaust it so we could gaff hook it up and over the transom. As soon as the highly irritated fish was aboard, it commenced to put forth a huge flipping and snapping and nipping at my mother's exposed toes.

At that time my mother proceeded to, as they say in show business, *bust a move.* She demonstrated some new dance steps more complicated than anything I had ever seen on American Bandstand. I had no idea she was so light on her feet as she kept one step ahead of the snapping jaws. At this point, I was forced to shoulder Dickie aside as he was beginning to moan gently while getting that special *mullet look.* I then began to massage the barracuda smartly about the head and shoulders with a cut-down two iron from my father's golf bag.

Luckily, my father kept several golf clubs on the boat in case he had a chance to drive some old junker balls off the stern when the fish weren't biting. The fish didn't bite for him a lot, and over the years he drove, sliced and hooked hundreds of old golf balls off the stern of Captain Crayton's other boat, *Miss Behavior.* In fact, I've heard local stories of a hammerhead shark that was caught just beyond Winyah Bay with one of my father's golf balls inside of it. I'm told the ball had the Georgetown County Chamber of Commerce Golf Tournament logo on it. I have no reason to doubt this.

In closing, Miss Gladys won the Georgetown County Woman's Fishing Derby that year and took home the $100 prize for catching the trophy-size 106-pound pit bull barracuda. The awesome fish outweighed her by six pounds. That trophy barracuda was stuffed, mounted and proudly displayed directly above her desk down at the offices of the Georgetown County Chamber of Commerce, where it may still be collecting dust to this day.

PART TWO

WORKING IN THE WOODS, HERE AND THERE AND ALL ABOUT

Rolling Thunder:
The Last Ride of the Sugar Barge

THIS IS THE TRUE STORY OF AN AUTOMOTIVE ADVENTURE that took place in a 1950 Buick Roadmaster Deluxe with Dynaflow Transmission and four portholes on each side of the hood. These portholes signified great status as they only appeared on the top of the Buick line, which was the Roadmaster Deluxe Series.

This particular Buick Roadmaster, known far and wide as *The Sugar Barge,* belonged to my elder brother, Dixon Roy Kilbourne, a Great American. It was the apple of his eye. It was his first official car, and he kept it cleaned and polished at all times. Unfortunately, his idea of keeping the car in excellent condition stopped with the exterior and did not involve anything that went on under the hood or beneath the car. I'm not sure if he had ever actually met the engine in person. He was not mechanically inclined, as they say, and figured if the car had gas in it, and as long as it was clean and polished, it should run fine until either the gas ran out or it got too dirty to run right.

By way of background, I had recently completed a short stint in the United States Marine Corps and had just begun working down in the swamps of the Savannah River as a Intern Forest Ranger while waiting to begin my college experience as a Forestry student at Clemson University, which is located in the great state of South Carolina.

I had been given this plum Forest Ranger Internship position because I was a close relative of my Sainted Mother. She worked as the church secretary for St. Thaddeus Episcopal Church, where one of the Deacons was a Mr. John B. Hatcher, who was also Supervisor of the Savannah River Forest and held the rank of GS (Government Service) 13. There was only one local official who was ranked above Mr. Hatcher and that was a Mr. A. A. Bomba, who held the exalted rank of GS 15 and was the overall Savannah River Plant General Manager. I believe the President of the United States, a federal employee, also held the rank of GS 15 at that time.

Somehow, as a result of my mother's maternal impulses, I had ended up in a carpool with all the Savannah River Forest Management Team. They were three gentlemen with whom I would be traveling to and from work every day. Within this elite group there was my direct boss, my direct boss' boss, and my direct boss' boss' boss. And then there was me. I wasn't anyone's boss. I look back now and blame my Sainted Mother for arranging my membership in this carpool. She would deeply regret brokering this agreement before the first week was out.

It should be noted that all of these three bosses owned very nice cars, all General Motors models that were considered to be *top of the line* and the proper automotive choice for *Captains of Industry*. This was before Japanese cars were invented. On the other hand, as a beginning college student, I had proud ownership of *The Ghost*, which was a Ford convertible of questionable age and provenance. One issue of concern regarding *The Ghost* was that the canvas top had caught fire during a late night event, which directly resulted from my elder brother playing with matches and fireworks while we were celebrating the Fourth of July the previous summer. It was at night and he thought the convertible top was in the down position. He never did have very good night vision. As a result, what remained of the top didn't fully protect the car's interior from the elements.

Thus it was that on the first day I was to be the designated driver, after my three carpool worthies had already taken their turns, I decided to ask my brother, Dixon Roy Kilbourne, a Great American, if he would consider loaning me his Buick Roadmaster Deluxe, also known as *The Sugar Barge*, so that I might not be embarrassed by delivering these gentles to their place of work in a raggedy-topped old Ford convertible.

The *Sugar Barge* was commodious in every respect, with a leathery backseat that could comfortably accommodate three fully-grown men or up to five medium-sized high school girls, if they were friends. In the face of my brother's skepticism, I swore a blood oath that I would return *The Sugar Barge* in the same fine condition that it was in when he reluctantly loaned it to me. This automobile was his pride and joy, as well as his primary means of attracting the sugary southern poon.

However, considering how perfect my brother thought the over-all condition of the *Barge* was, it should be noted that I had recently overheard him complaining about the car not always wanting to stop when he engaged the brakes. He wondered if it might have anything to do with the fact that the gas tank was less than half full. Also, he had not washed it for several days. As mentioned earlier, he was in no way mechanically inclined. I assumed that the brake pads needed replac-ing or the brake drums needed turning but didn't want to go into this automotive mechanics discussion with him, as it would cause him undue concern about loaning the car to me.

It might be worth observing at this point that the prodigious *Sugar Barge,* with the four portholes on each side of the hood, was unusually large by current automotive standards. It had an overall weight of two-and-one-half tons, which made it 5,000 pounds of rolling thunder on the hoof. Due to the sheer size of the *Barge,* the gas tank required one gallon of gas for every ten miles of travel. Luckily this was not a big issue as gas was only 25 cents per gallon, unless there was a *gas war,* in which case it would sell for considerably less.

The *Sugar Barge* was not designed for speed and took nearly ten minutes on a well-paved road with a slight downhill angle to achieve its maximum velocity of ninety miles per hour. Unfortunately, it took even longer to bring it to a full stop once it was rolling along. It was not an especially responsive automobile and tended to surge and float at top speed. Under the most ideal conditions, a full mile of open road-way was required to slow down and stop this shiny black behemoth. The upside of a steep hill always helped.

The Sugar Barge provided a large volume of aural gratification. My eldest brother, Dixon Roy Kilbourne, a Great American, was proud of the Barge's deep rumble and had recently invested $120 in a pair of Dynatone mufflers to achieve same. While underway, the car produced a sound similar to several hippos with digestive issues mating in a wind tunnel. He believed the elusive southern poon was sent into elevated states of ecstasy, and agreement, while seated in the commodious rear seat with the engine running and the Dynatones singing their rumbling song of love. Johnny Mathis would be crooning his passionate feelings on the radio.

Well, so here we were, if you can visualize this. I had now picked up my three carpooling worthies who were all each other's boss of some kind and certified *Captains of Industry*. They had at least one thing in common, and that was the fact that each and every one of them was my boss at some level or other. I liked my new job and was desirous of keeping it for a while yet. I needed some of the government's money to pay for my college tuition at Clemson during the coming year.

Everything went fairly well on the drive to the Savannah River Plant. In fact, we were even a few minutes early since the gas pedal got stuck to the floorboard about halfway there. I had to take the *Barge* out of gear and coast to a stop while dragging my foot before I could reach down and pull the gas pedal loose. "This car sure is a hard charger," said Mr. Wilton Stansbury, the wittier of the back-seat passengers and the boss of my direct boss. Mr. Wilton Stansbury was well known for his eccentric habit of wishing everyone a pleasant day a full fifteen minutes prior to reaching our destination. After his premature comment, he would then maintain strict silence while resting his hand on the door handle and working it up and down. He was different in that way.

Although we were warned that a storm was on the way, the following eight hours at work went by uneventfully while I carried out my Forest Ranger job, which involved dealing death to reptiles and serpents while the rest of the crew sloshed around in the knee-deep swamp water marking pine trees to be cut and converted into pulp, and then into cardboard (probably, we had all agreed, for Tampon boxes). I spent the lunch hour applying goose grease to the gas pedal linkage so we wouldn't get back home nearly as quickly as we had gotten to work.

Concerning the growing weather, throughout the day the storm had been building up and there were fierce gale-force winds blowing by the time lunch was over. I began to develop a vague sense of uneasiness and a strong premonition that the day still had more excitement in store. My concerns were not addressed.

At five o'clock sharp we loaded back up in *The Sugar Barge* with high hopes for an uneventful trip home. I assured the various bosses that the gas pedal linkage issue had been seen to. Everything progressed smoothly for the first half of our trip, until the headwinds took on biblical proportions and there came up a storm like unto that which Noah and his host of pets endured. The winds increased yet again and *The Sugar Barge's* massive black hood, with the four portholes on each side, began to quiver and then rattle. I slowed down to 60 mph and began coasting when we started down a pretty steep incline in the road. *The Sugar Barge* seemed to increase speed rather than decrease, and I gently began applying the brakes. The brake pedal felt mushy and went almost all the way to the floorboard. Not an encouraging sign. I began calculating how many miles it would take for us to roll to a stop from this speed and figured we didn't have enough distance even if we rolled all the way through town and then on into Georgetown County. Dragging my foot definitely wasn't going to help this time.

Meanwhile, the ominous hood rattle had developed further into a clamorous thumping as we drove headlong into the increasing storm while the *Barge* continued to pick up speed. There was a distinct undercurrent of tension throughout the car, although nothing was said. It would have been hard to be heard within the car anyway, as the Dynatones were rumbling even louder than usual. However, unlike the young high school sugar shorts, the bosses were not moved to ecstasy over the deep and sweet rumbling sound of the custom mufflers.

At this point we briskly rolled by the new Cadillac car recently purchased by Mr. A. A. Bomba, the overall Plant Manager, who was everyone's boss except the President of the United States. Mr. John B. Hatcher made troubled eye contact with him and nodded a tense greeting as we rumbled and thumped by. Mr. A. A. Bomba was not accustomed to being passed, by anyone.

Just as we re-entered the right-hand lane, directly in front of Mr. A. A. Bomba's proud new Cadillac car, the rattling and thumping abruptly ceased. It became eerily quiet in the car as a heavy silence happened. Then for a split second it became dark as a large shadow seemed to pass over us. It looked like one of those giant black manta rays that you see on the *Discovery Channel* on Saturday afternoons. The shadow thing was about the size of a fully-grown Volkswagen. The heavy silence continued, as everyone seemed to hold his breath. Mr. Wilton Stansbury had his hand firmly attached to the door handle. Then, Mr. Al Tofte, my immediate boss, who was a person given to understatements said, "Did anyone happen to see that?" His immediate boss, Mr. Wilton Stansbury asked, "What was that thing that just flew over us?"

Just then there occurred a huge grinding crash immediately behind us. It sounded like you might expect two freight trains hauling hogs would sound if they collided head-on. Then there occurred a lot of squealing and squalling, much like hogs fighting over grits and buttermilk on a hot August day.

As I looked through the windshield, there appeared to be a large part missing of what was my elder brother's favorite possession in this world, and a proven attractor of the wily southern poon. As I glanced in the rearview mirror, I observed the gigantic black hood of *The Sugar Barge,* with four portholes on each side, fly directly into the grill and windshield of Mr. A. A. Bomba's brand new Cadillac car. I am thinking that nothing good is going to come of this when Mr. Al Tofte, my immediate boss, said in his understated way, "I think Bomba just ran over your car's hood."

Mr. John B. Hatcher, the boss of us all said, "Maybe we should stop." This sounded like excellent advice except that the gas pedal was stuck again and the brakes had finally given up. This would have been a great time to find a steep hill going up, but unfortunately we were just beginning a two-mile downgrade. We were still three miles from home and gaining traction on the downhill slope.

It was just about this time that Mr. Wilton Stansbury, my boss' boss, absently remarked that he hoped we all had a pleasant evening. He then placed his hand on the door handle and proceeded to abandon *The Sugar Barge.* He casually commented that he would see us all in the morning as he tumbled out of sight.

Typical lunch break mischief. Author takes his turn at Turkey in the Straw with small pet alligator while co-worker Harvey Key calls out square dance steps. This activity was strongly frowned upon by OSHA.

Hard Hats and Hip Boots:
A Summer Spent Rattlesnake Wrangling
In the Savannah River Swamp

ONCE I SPENT AN ENTIRE SUMMER WRANGLING REPTILES and serpents in the Savannah River Swamp. You may have heard about alligator wrestling in Florida; however, this was not that. This was authentic reptile wrangling in the swampy state of Georgia. My job as wrangler was to control and confine the local serpents, thus assuring the safety of my crewmembers. If I couldn't confine and/or control the serpents, I shot them fatally dead.

The area in which we worked was characterized by quicksand bogs and mosquitoes as large as swamp geese. It was so swampy that the filming of the iconic movie, *Creature from the Black Lagoon,* had to be done farther down the river where the conditions were less severe for the creature.

This unusual job opportunity occurred immediately after my release from a tour with the United States Marine Corps and just before my beginning college at Clemson University, in the great state of South Carolina, where I planned to eventually complete a degree in Forestry.

The plan was for me to work as a summer laborer on the US Forest Service District of the Savannah River Project. This was in the beautiful state of Georgia, which, according to the license plates, referred to itself as *The Peach State.* I always assumed this was because of the unusual preponderance of beautiful women who were born and raised up in Georgia. It might also have had something to do with fruit from there, but that fact didn't interest us young and lusty swampers. But I digress.

I was to begin as a member of the Timber Stand Improvement (TSI) Crew, at the attractive beginning pay scale of $3.85 per hour, before taxes. The idea was to save all my money to pay for a year of college when September rolled around. This swamp work was in great demand and I was only able to get the job because I was a close relative of my Sainted Mother, who had been a church secretary there for many years. The Forest Supervisor went to our church and was a friend of hers.

Somehow, as a result of my mother's overactive maternal impulses, I also ended up in an unlikely carpool with all the Savannah River Forest Management Team. However, within the first week, there occurred a very bad carpool-related thing that happened to myself and this group of worthies. Suffice it to say, my Sainted Mother deeply regretted arranging for me to be in a carpool with these gentles. But that dark event is covered in greater detail in the previous story entitled *Rolling Thunder: The Last Ride of the Sugar Barge.* Enough said on that horrific tragedy.

The following story describes events which occurred during those months in the swamp, while working with a collection of truly strange and bizarre characters.

John Carver, the Senior Crew Foreman, and Bill Story, the Junior Grade Foreman, were next-door neighbors. These two characters were always in an ongoing game of one-upsmanship, which had been going on for years. John was the boss and very squared away. Bill, not nearly so squared away, was the crew clown. They had been working together in these swamps for a decade or more. Both were in their thirties and both were married. John considered himself a *family man*, as he had more children than he could keep track of. Bill, on the other hand, had no family other than his bride, Billie Sue Story. Bill had been working extra hard to get his wife pregnant and wasn't having any luck. John told him that he had the answer to getting Billie Sue in a family way. Bill was very interested and asked for further details. John said, "Y'all just have to get her all ready and in the proper position, and then y'all open the bedroom window and holler for me, and I'll take care of the rest."

Another memorable character was Glenn Franklin, who was known as the *Old Man*. Although Glenn couldn't tell time, someone had given him a very nice pocket watch for Christmas. He carried it proudly to work in the swamps every day. Someone was always facetiously asking him what time it was, and Glenn would haul that big watch out of his pocket and proudly hold it directly in front of the person's face and say, "There is what time it is."

On the TSI crew, we were known as the crew that went out early and came back late. We were mandated to take a ten-minute break every hour, whether we wanted to or not. When break time arrived, we just dropped where we stopped and smoked a cigarette. If a worker didn't smoke, he chewed. The chewers were messier than the smokers and generally had tobacco drippings staining their beards and work clothes. They were not the type of user tobacco companies would feature in their advertising.

The TSI work involved eradicating certain kinds of hardwoods out of the ecosystem. The primary tool was a *poison gun*, which was a hollow steel tube filled with a lethal mixture of diesel fuel as a carrier and a nasty dose of 245T, which I believe was used in Viet Nam as a defoliant. The TSI gun weighed about fifteen pounds when it was full of poison. The worker would girdle the target tree by slamming the razor-sharp, rounded tip of the gun into the base of the tree, pry back to form a cup and then turn the trigger on the handle to release a few ounces of poison into the cup. The target tree had to be completely circled with a series of overlapping cups in order to be killed. The dying process usually took a few months and then the foliage would brown out and drop off.

The most interesting position on the TSI crew was simply referred to on the job as the *Gunner*. The official bureaucratic government job title was *Crew Gunner, Level II, Snakes*. This was usually a crewmember familiar with firearms since his job was to carry the 12-gauge shotgun and blast apart poisonous snakes that threatened the rest of the crew. After working on the TSI Crew for four weeks, and satisfactorily completing the probationary period, I was promoted to the *Gunner* position since I had just gotten out of the Marines and was highly trained with all sorts of firearms and other implements of destruction.

Tools of the trade—weapon of mass snake destruction and personal hardhat. Note official title on hat: Crew Gunner, Level II, Snakes. Hat still contains trace amounts of swamp mud and snake DNA juices.

The *Gunner, Level II* would walk out in front of the crew that worked in a line, about ten feet apart from each other. The entire line was usually sixty to seventy feet wide as it moved through the swamp. The Gunner called out, "Here snakey, here snakey," as he walked ahead of the crew. I would be kept on the run from one side of the crew line to the other as the cry of "Snake!" rang out through the swampy woods. At that point, I had to hustle over and shoot the offending serpent directly in the head.

In fact, the *Gunner* actually didn't have to be especially skilled or accurate with his work since your typical reptile responds to heat and motion with split-second accuracy. I just had to fire the shotgun blast in the general vicinity of the snake's head, and the reptile would do the rest by striking at the load of pellets coming out of the business end of the shotgun. The serpents made even a rookie gunner look like a sharpshooter.

The four main poisonous reptiles native to the general habitat we worked in were your cottonmouth water moccasin, your timber rattler, your copperhead, and your coral snake, which was the smallest and the most deadly with a personal venom that would paralyze a fully-grown swamp troll within forty-five seconds.

After a few weeks of being the *Crew Gunner, Level II, Snakes,* I was able to actually smell a snake from ten or fifteen feet away. Your rattlesnakes and your cottonmouth water moccasins were the most pungent and smelled like a combination of old gym socks and a ripe mullet. Your mullet is a nasty-smelling ocean-dwelling fish common to the *low country* area of South Carolina. Trust me, you never want to eat a mullet under any circumstances.

All the crewmembers were required to attend regular safety training sessions, which were almost always devoted to poisonous snake training. We were all required to carry a personal-size Cutter Snakebite Kit, which was a rounded rubber tube about the size of a fat man's thumb. The tube opened in the middle and contained a fine nylon cord for a tourniquet as well as a razor/scalpel sort of device.

There was also a little set of instructions containing an amusing story about what would happen to your arm, or your foot, if you didn't loosen the tourniquet at regular intervals. Basically the message promised that the limb would dry up and fall off if the directions weren't carefully followed. The rubber halves of the snakebite kit would be used to suck the venom out after several ugly X-shaped incisions were made on the wound, and the blood was flowing freely.

In addition to the individual personal snakebite kits for each crewmember, the crew chief was responsible for seeing that a twenty-gallon can of ice and water was always in one of the crew vehicles to be used as another snakebite treatment tool, if necessary. After using the snakebite kit, with the cutting, the sucking, the restriction by tourniquet and the reading of the graphic warning, the victim was forced to immerse the wound in ice water while he was rushed to the hospital, which could be twenty or more miles away, depending on what part of the swamp we were working in on that particular day.

No snakebite, in the history of snakebites, has ever been as painful as keeping an injured hand, or foot, fully immersed in freezing water. The purpose of this torture was to bring the temperature of the wound site down to near freezing, or below, thus greatly slowing down or stopping the blood flow, and consequently the venom flow.

There is no other pain similar to what is suffered during this hellish process. Snakebite victims sometimes beg to be allowed to die rather than be subjected to the ice-water torture. Their thinking was that once they were allowed to die, the tortured limb could then be taken out of the ice water and the excruciating pain would be over. However, according to OSHA guidelines, the victim was not to be allowed to die, and therefore we insisted on keeping the injured body part fully immersed all the way to the hospital while we enjoyed a break from the swamps. We usually drove slowly in order to extend our work break for as long as possible.

We all had our personal snake stories. Everyone's story featured a snake that was considerable larger, and more venomous, than any snake featured in any other crewmember's story. While I worked on this crew, I heard of snakes as large as a fully grown bandersnatch. I still have a set of rattles somewhere, which had a record-breaking twenty-one rattles and a button and measured nearly four inches long. These were not baby rattles. These were big boy rattles. The previous owner of the string of rattles was a brutish serpent that weighed nearly twenty pounds and was thick as a fat man's thigh.

As United States federal workers, we were mandated, by some random law, to take a ten-minute break every hour—something or other about OSHA and heat stroke. We also took a thirty-minute break for lunch. This was when the royal BS really started to get deep. It was lucky that we all wore hip boots! There is nothing like working with a bored crew where each crewmember is trying to outdo the others with extravagant statements and ludicrous challenges. Since I was the new guy on this well-established crew, the competition to see who could get me to believe the most outlandish story was fierce. The stories ranged from the size of some mythological reptile of *biblical proportions* to the report that a crewmember had very possibly been *abducted by aliens* over the past weekend.

At this point, I have to admit freely, and without shame or regret, that I was personally involved in one elaborate prank myself. This practical joke targeted a crewmember who talked incessantly about his new Volkswagen. This little car was supposed to achieve previously unheard-of gas economy. He claimed he got over fifty miles per gallon, even while driving into a strong headwind.

He held forth on the merits of this car from a miles-per-gallon point of view for so long, and so loud, that we conspired to play a certain diabolic trick upon him. Every day, while he was out in the swamps with the crew, we would arrange for someone back at headquarters to pour a gallon or so of gas into his proud new Volkswagen's gas tank. This was in the olden days when gas tanks didn't have locking caps. Who cared about locking up gas? It only cost a quarter a gallon at the more expensive stations where they washed your windshield and checked your oil. That's why we used to call them *service stations*.

We kept up the top-secret gas transfusions for a week or so until we had his tank overflowing. We casually asked him if he had been keeping track of the miles per gallon he had been enjoying. He was hesitant to confess that, yes, the gas mileage was excellent, but he was concerned because the car seemed to somehow be manufacturing gas rather than using it. He reported that gas was actually overflowing from his tank even though he hadn't stopped at a service station all week! He was going to take the car back to the dealership over the weekend to have the engine checked to see if this phenomenon was possible. He also wondered if one of us would like to buy some of his surplus gas.

It was easy to tell which crewmembers were married because they always showed up with what we called a *wife lunch* that might contain fried chicken, biscuits and gravy, salad, iced tea, and even dessert. We bachelors most likely consumed several fried fruit pies or a chocolated moon pie and a warm soft drink. We salivated over the married guy's lunches, but not enough to make us consider giving up our bachelor status. We always evened things out when we came to work on Monday mornings and described, in great and colorful detail, all the mischief we had been into over the weekend. Often our reports involved simultaneous activities with numerous members of the opposite sex, all at the same time!

During the mandated ten-minute breaks, the conversation would focus on exactly what the challenges would be during the upcoming thirty-minute lunch period. Often the lunchtime betting would get so fast and furious that little time was left to actually eat. Several of the more dedicated gamblers would eat their moon pies standing up while throwing hatchets or tossing rocks. When all other betting ideas had been exhausted, someone would want to bet on some event as random as whether a particular chipmunk would dart left or dart right as we approached it, or whether the next reptile we encountered would be a water moccasin or a timber rattler.

A sampling of the standard, everyday gambling contests that occupied us most lunchtimes follows:

The Throwing of the Hatchet: The hatchet-throwing contest, one of the most popular events, actually took a fair amount of skill. Why we were all required to carry individual, very sharp and dangerous hatchets was never revealed to us. They hung from our belts, suspended in a sort of leather holster arrangement. I can't think of any occasion where we used them for any purpose other than to contest against each other during our lunch breaks.

My very good friend, and former high school classmate, Harvey Monroe Key, A Great American and Southern Gentleman, was surprisingly good at this challenge. He could stick a hatchet in a fat poplar tree from twenty paces back, three times out of four. Unfortunately, on the one out of four times when he missed, the hatchet would ricochet interestingly off the tree and come flying back into the crew. For some reason, no one ever seemed to think this activity might be dangerous or might be frowned upon by OSHA. I don't know how we would have explained how it came about that one of our crewmembers had to be rushed to the hospital with a hatchet stuck into his forehead and his head stuck down in the ice bucket. I guess that's why we were required to wear hard hats.

Heads or Tails: Coin flipping. The person who lost always loudly protested that the coin hadn't been flipped properly and invariably demanded that the contest be extended to best two out of three. Always. This was a given. You could bet on it.

Tree Measurements: Offering to guess the diameter of a tree was a sure way to get Bill Story to put up a dollar. He rarely came within six inches of the accurate measurement and lost an average of ten dollars a week on this daily wager.

Gator Cone Toss: Even throwing pinecones at alligators floating peacefully in the lake became a wager-worthy activity. As in, "I'll bet you a dollar I can bounce a cone off that gator's head quicker than you can." A typical response was, "Oh yeah? Well, let's see your money, Mr. Big Talker!"

A playful alligator encourages unwary swamp workers to come in for a quick dip to cool off during the daily lunch break. Note pinecone bumps on top of head.

The Holding of the Breath Contest: When we had run out of all other contests to bet on, someone was always willing to bet they could hold their breath longer than someone else. Whoever held his breath the longest earned a dollar from the challenger. Your heavy smokers were handicapped in this event, but they never considered opting out. Bill Story was a heavy smoker. He always lost. A two-year-old, one-lunged midget with emphysema could handily beat Bill Story at this contest.

It is important to keep in mind that these were grown men carrying on this way! Betting on who could hold their breath the longest. Furthermore, they would actually go home and brag to their wives about these challenges over dinner!

I was having so much fun working with this zany group of characters that by the end of that long, hot summer, I postponed my college schedule for a year to stay on working with them. I enjoyed two fat raises, which came to slightly over $5.00 per hour, plus whatever I could win while gambling with Bill Story. Billie Sue

Story finally got herself in a family way, and none of us asked for specific details of that blessed event.

We were *grown-up kids* living the great American dream, tramping about in the Savannah River Swamps in hip boots and hard hats. Throwing hatchets, shooting reptiles and holding our breath on a dollar bet. Life was good.

Up on Timber Mountain Lookout Tower, on the Kaniksu National Forest, located on the Washington-Canadian border, in 1961. Photo taken by lovely lady helicopter pilot, Big Mildred, who dropped in on the last day of the fire season to help close up the tower. Wisely, she never turned her back on me the entire time.

Being on the Lookout

I WAS JUST FINISHING MY FRESHMAN YEAR at Clemson University in South Carolina where I was majoring in Forestry, and I was wondering what I would be doing for the summer. In those days the National Forest Service and the Clemson Forestry Department traditionally worked together to guarantee any full-time Forestry student a variety of summer jobs on one of the many National Forests spread throughout the country.

For my first summer as a full-fledged Clemson Forestry student going into my sophomore year, I was offered a job as a Fireman II on the Kaniksu National Forest, which was located on the Washington-Canadian border, or option #2, the position of *rattlesnake wrangler* working in the Savannah River Swamps, which was a job I had already worked at previously, but that's another story.

I wasn't sure what a Fireman II did for a living as the job description was fairly vague, but I was pretty sure it would be more pleasant than wrestling serpents. Plus I had never been farther west than East Georgia, and the thought of getting out of the hot and humid South for the summer had a definite appeal. The Fireman II description did mention that the applicant must not suffer from either a fear of small-enclosed spaces or a fear of heights. This clause should have raised a big red flag, but for some reason it got by me.

After a very eventful cross-country adventure in a 1960 Oldsmobile Deluxe *topless* convertible car, I arrived in Newport, Washington, and reported in for work. I was informed that I would be manning a fire tower on Timber Mountain for fourteen weeks, more or less, depending on the timing of the first snowfall, which usually occurred in mid-September.

During the brief training period for new fire tower operators, I learned that my job would be to complete a 360-degree visual search with the provided binoculars every hour on the hour and to make radio contact with the ranger station every four hours during the day. Other than the mandatory reports down to the Ranger Station, the rest of the time was mine to use in any way that might be considered *safe and sane* by a normal person.

There were eight towers in all on the Kaniksu as this forest was classified as *fire extreme,* which was one notch above *fire intense* and not such good news to us rookie tower operators. We would be well broken in by the time most of us came back down in mid-September. One rookie couldn't hack it and had to be brought down mid-way through his second week of the season. Looking back, he may have demonstrated more good sense than those of us who stayed on. I know for a fact the permanent twitch I have suffered from for the past forty years is a direct result of the trauma I endured spending fourteen weeks perched atop the Timber Mountain Lookout Tower, in the Kaniksu National Forest on the Washington-Canadian border. I refer to my condition as the Timber Mountain Twitch.

I learned several important facts during the training period. There would be no electricity and no water on my tower. Furthermore, the nearest dirt road connecting the tower to civilization was more than five miles away. I would have to hike in, assuming I could locate the tower, and then hike out again when the first snows came, which was not time certain. All my supplies, including food, as well as anything else that would be judged to be *reasonable* (in other words no dancing girls) would be delivered by helicopter on a bi-weekly basis.

I was to complete a form indicating what foods I would like to be supplied with for the next three months. The choices were pretty much limited to canned food, such as tuna, beans, Vienna sausages, sardines, and Chef Boyardee spaghetti and meatballs by the case, as well as your dried food essentials such as potatoes, rice, bread, flour, etc.

All the food would be delivered at cost to me and would come by the case from the local grocer. I would pay the bill when I came down in the fall.

The only medicine I had on the lookout for that long summer was one case of a very hearty ale, very similar to today's Sierra Nevada Bigfoot Ale, which I had a prescription for in case of snakebite, bear attack, or some other medical emergency.

My supplies would be delivered by helicopter every two weeks, and I would have to call in my order 48 hours in advance of the delivery time. The food and other supplies would be lowered down to me in a net attached to the helicopter by a cable. I was sternly warned not to try and get in the net and attempt to have an escape.

The weekend before I was to hike in and open up the tower, I went to the local library and applied for a card, which would be good for the rest of the year. I also checked out fourteen books with the understanding that someone from the ranger station would return them in two weeks and pick up a new set of books from the fiction shelves, beginning alphabetically for lack of a better way to select books. The books would be delivered to me along with my other provisions every two weeks.

By the time I returned to the library at the end of September, I had read through all the A's and was well into the B's. Pearl S. Buck's *The Good Earth* was the last book I read for that summer. The sympathetic librarian also thoughtfully provided me with a pamphlet explaining how to cook *survival style* on a wood stove with only the bare essentials. I recall one of the first chapter recipes involved the meat of a *mature o'possum.* After extensive research, I would not recommend that recipe unless a tender young o'possum is substituted for the mature one.

I finally found the tower after a day's hike, lugging my old Marine Corps duffle bag containing all my worldly belongings. The tower was so tall that I could see it for several miles away, which provided much assistance in my locating it. As I climbed up the stairs, all 110 of them, and opened the door, I was greeted by a sort of magical space, exactly 12′ x 12′ and enclosed entirely in glass. As I entered the little tower room for the first time, I saw there was a basic military cot with a thin mattress and a rolled-up sleeping bag, no pillow. There was also a desk in one corner and a woodstove along the north wall. I tried to imagine living in this 144 square feet of space for the entire summer.

There was also a two-person table and chairs for those fine dining experiences with me, myself, and I that I was looking forward to. Later in the season, under intense lightning storm pressure and weak from starvation, I was moved to *create* a dish so excessive in proportions and ingredients that I named it *Rice Orgy.* Little did I know that I would still be enjoying this concoction of wretched excess forty years later, though the name has long since been upgraded to the more elegant *Rice Orgy Parisienne,* but that's another story.

In addition to these most basic furnishings, there was an Osborne Fire Finder bolted to the floor in the exact middle of the room. This would be my primary tool used to specifically locate and report lightning strikes and signs of smoke. There was also a three-foot-wide catwalk surrounding the tower room on all sides, which would come in very handy if one were to experience an inconvenient bladder pressure in the middle of the night. The official tower bathroom was an outhouse on the ground located a fair distance from the tower. I had to learn to plan ahead.

As I looked out of the tower for the first time, I realized that I had never seen so many trees all in one sweeping view. They were as thick as grass on a golf course putting green. I also realized that I was personally responsible for each and every one of them. They were my trees! By the end of the summer I had reported over two hundred lightning strikes and twice that many sightings of smoke, mostly from campfires. I had not lost a single one of my personal trees and felt pretty heroic about all that.

After several weeks on the tower I had fallen into the grip of a great lassitude. About the only break in the tedium of my typical day on the tower was my radio call to the Ranger Station down in Newport every four hours. I suppose they wanted to be sure I hadn't fallen off the tower or been attacked by a rutting moose or something similar. A typical report, which I always began very officially, would go something like this: "This is the Timber Mountain Lookout checking in. No smoke sighted. Nothing seems to be on fire." At this point in the conversation, I would begin to lose it. "Now get me down from here STAT! I think I am having an attack of appendicitis or maybe the epizooty. If you will send the resupply helicopter for me right now," I would plead, "I promise I'll come right back up early in the morning. Help! I think I see a rabid bear down below. Can you hear me? Breaker! Breaker! Come in Ranger Station!"

The answer was always a laconic, "That's nice, Timber Mountain. That's what you said just this morning. Now you know there are no rabid bears this time of year, and we would really appreciate your holding on for only another twelve and one-half weeks more. Now quit playing with yourself and get back to work. Newport Ranger Station out." The evil dispatcher down at the Ranger station was a certified sadist whose biggest pleasure in life was reminding us lookout tower operators how much more time we had on the tower before the season was mercifully over.

These days and weeks were extremely lonely for such a gregarious person as myself and, if truth be told, after eight weeks or so on the mountain, I had developed something of a crush on the helicopter pilot during her bi-weekly supply visits as she was the only human I would see for the entire fourteen weeks.

My deep yearning to begin a meaningful relationship with her might have been because she was my only connection to civilization. That, and the fact that she drove that helicopter in a wild and sexy sort of way. I recall that on one occasion, I screamed up to her and gestured wildly, as she hovered above while lowering my supplies down in a net.

"Hello! My name is Dave! What is your name! Can you come down for a visit? I have a nice young o'possum stew and some candles!" She couldn't hear my words due to the sound of the rotors, but she always shouted back to me, "Stand back! Don't try to get into the net and have an Es Cape!"

I later learned that her name was Big Mildred. On my last day on the tower she dropped by to take away one helicopter load of supplies that the Ranger station didn't want to leave up on the lookout over the winter. As she climbed down from the helicopter I saw that she was built like a Clemson linebacker and looked like she could hold her own in a bar fight. I suppose I should be thankful that she didn't accept my romantic offer of a fine young o'possum stew dinner, complete with candles, but you never know how it might have turned out. Romance was in the air until she was on the ground, so to speak.

The Discovery of Rice Orgy Parisienne

WE HAVE ALL HEARD THE OLD SAYING, *Necessity is the mother of invention.* The following exciting little story chronicles the events and activities that occurred during the mother of all electrified ice storms. This mothering weather event caused the historic discovery of *Rice Orgy Parisienne,* which is good to eat in times of great emergency.

Once upon a time, in a land far, far away, I spent a long summer up on a United States Forest Service lookout tower on the Washington-Canadian border. During my third month on Timber Mountain, at 6,500 feet elevation, a three-day storm of historic proportions blew down for a visit from above the Arctic Circle. The storm was full of ice and was electrified as well. It had my complete attention. The wind was gusting at sixty miles per hour and my little cabin at the top of the tower, up at eighty-four feet, where the air is rare, was bucking and swaying under the relentless force of the wind. The cabin itself measured a mere 12 feet by 12 feet or about the size of a large pantry but without the food. This cozy little space was my home for fourteen long and lonely weeks. I never want to go back up there again, ever.

Throughout the storm, the three-inch-diameter steel anchoring cables, which were supposed to keep the tower upright, were thrumming and humming, and I was personally quaking and shaking. I was feeling pretty desolate and decidedly unsafe. I recorded over two hundred separate lightning strikes within a seventy-two-hour period using the Osborne Firefinder, which is a sort of waist-high table compass arrangement bolted to the exact center of the lookout cabin.

As the storm persisted into the second day, I became weakened by famishment. The strikes were coming down so hot and heavy that I couldn't leave the firefinder to fix anything to eat. The lookout tower had no electricity so I cooked everything on a primitive two-hole wood-burning iron box that served as both the cabin's sole heat source and its cooking stove. I am sure that cave dwellers, during the early Paleolithic Era, had more advanced cooking and heating methods than the United States Forest Service provided me during my summer on Timber Mountain.

By dodging back and forth in between lightning strikes, I somehow managed to get a fire started and some water boiling. After the water was fully cooked, I threw in an entire three-pound bag of instant rice. Actually, I only threw in the contents of the bag. I saved the bag because I needed to keep the complicated cooking instructions. *Use one cup of rice and two cups water, then heat and eat.* I was a bachelor sort of person and not used to cooking complicated dishes requiring specific measurements. After the rice was cooked, I dumped in six cans of tuna fish–just the fish, not the cans.[1] I also added five pounds of chopped cheddar cheese to the recipe.

To complete the new emergency recipe, I also threw in four cans of green peas that I had been using as weights to hold down the corners of a rolled topographical map. At this point, I had committed pretty much everything I had on hand to this questionable combination of proteins and carbohydrates.

The mixing of the rice, tuna, cheese and peas, which is not a combination normally occurring in nature, resulted in a large pot of very unattractive, but possibly edible stuff. In fact, it was so nasty-looking

---

[1] Although I strongly prohibited myself from eating any fish products after being force-fed schools of mullet fish during my vulnerable early years while living on Pawleys Island, I feel that tuna in a can isn't actually fish since it is categorized as "canned meat" by the folks down at the supermarket. Other items that share the canned meat shelf with your canned tuna are the jowls of hogs, the feet of pigs, your canned Spam, and those little cans of deviled ham products. After careful testing, I can assure you that any/all fishiness has been processed out of the canned tuna. I guess they sell the fish taste and smell separately.

that I couldn't force myself to gaze directly upon it. Luckily, I had a bottle of French dressing that I wasn't using, so I covered up the surface of the whole steaming, bubbling, and heaving mess with that. I now had a big ugly, orange-ish mess, which was only a slight improvement. I crept up upon this devil's admixture, and very hesitantly (set to the tune of *Love Potion #9*) *I held my nose, I closed my eyes, I took a taste.* I reasoned that forcing myself to eat this would be good for my character development. However, I was shocked and surprised to find out that it was actually very tasty. How could this be? How could anything that looked so very bad, taste so very good?

I brought a large steaming bowl of the stuff over to the fire-finder and began to methodically shovel it into my feeding hole while still keeping track of lightning strikes. After fifteen minutes of non-stop character development, I was so bloated with this mixture that I could barely waddle around the little fire tower cabin. Unknowingly, I had just discovered a protein-rich foodstuff that I would continue to eat at least once a month for the next forty years, for a grand total of four hundred and eighty times, give or take a bowl or two. However, I did learn to reduce the measurements of necessary ingredients for future batches. For example, one cup of rice instead of one 3-pound bag works well nowadays.

The high-class name of this elegant new gourmet discovery was to be *Rice Orgy Parisienne*, in keeping with the absolute wretched excessiveness and guilty pleasure associated with the whole sort of ravenous consumption of this devil's mixture. That and the liberal use of your French dressing, which provides the specific Parisian flavor.

Over the intervening years, I have tried this recipe out on several members of my family, including Savannah A. Kilbourne, my number one daughter. In the past Savannah has made her opinion of this exotic dish crystal clear by declaring a number of times that she would not touch it with a woogie snatcher, much less with any part of her digestive system. She said it looks evil and seems somehow alive. She went on to say it looked *flushable*. How sharper than a serpent's tooth.

On the other hand, my excellent and more adventurous god-daughter, Amorikate Palmer, a highly evolved individual, has a very special place in her heart for *Rice Orgy Parisienne*. She is so favorably inclined toward this magical recipe that she believes it has supernatural restorative powers. She was once in an auto accident, not her fault, and called me before she drove away with the cute ambulance driver. She asked if I could possibly bring a six-quart saucepan of the palliative substance to the corner of Sixth and Main so that she could take it with her into the hospital. She was always one to plan ahead.

Several decades later, after years of intense counseling that was required to overcome the psychological trauma of my summer upon Timber Mountain, I was asked to write a food column in the local newspaper. Why I was singled out for this dubious recognition has never been fully understood. Perhaps it was because I was dating Elane Ahnemann, a lovely young woman of German heritage who worked down at the newspaper office at that time. The column was entitled *Chef David's Recipe of the Week*. By popular demand, one of the first recipes featured in this column was my *Rice Orgy Parisienne* concoction.

My adjective-rich *Rice Orgy* recipe, which received a favorable response from throughout the community's more adventurous cooks, was worded as follows:

Rice Orgy is a savory blending of long-grain rice, succulent fresh green peas, extra sharp cheddar, and the finest ocean-fresh albacore, using the center cut only. This mixture is to be gently enlivened with exotic herbs and spices from the Orient, such as your high-end salts and peppers, in order to provide the diner with a most interesting flavor contrast." The recipe went on to caution, "If the cook finds the

appearance or texture of the resulting entrée to be in any way offen-
sive or off-putting, the covering of the completed dish with a liberal
coating of French dressing is highly recommended. Serve with a gen-
erous portion of thick red wine for maximum benefit.

The simplicity of this meal is a thing of beauty. A steaming, heaping plate of your *Rice Orgy Parisienne* and a pint jar of hearty red table wine is all that is required. With this elegant menu, the diner is set for the evening, and well into the next day. In fact, no further sustenance will be required for the subsequent twenty-four hour period since full bed rest is prescribed.

The mud splattered, thrown, dragged and stepped-upon author, alongside the not-so-heroic Pinto Number Two who was just terrified by a smallish stick snake while innocently cantering into the Lost Meadows area of beautiful Lassen Volcanic National Park in northern California. Photo, circa 1965.

Pinto the Wonder Horse Rides Again

WHEN I WAS A YOUNG BOY of about twelve years, growing up in the lovely community of Aiken, in the great state of South Carolina, I took myself to the Saturday morning picture show at the Patricia Theatre downtown on Laurens Street every week.

In addition to the *feature film*, which was usually a Dean Martin and Jerry Lewis comedy or a western featuring cowboy heroes such as Roy Rogers, Gene Autry, the Lone Ranger, or the bullwhip-slinging Lash Larue, there also was a short *serial*. This was a fifteen-minute episode featuring some heroic character who was always vanquishing the bad guys while saving the good ones. The serial came on after the previews, but before the main feature, and often was the main reason that we went to the Saturday morning picture show every week without fail. If you missed a Saturday, you missed an installment of the serial story, and that was not good. There was no rewind in those days.

Many of my friends favored serial heroes like Buck Rogers, who was sort of an early spaceman/astronaut type, or Sky King who fought the bad guys while piloting a small plane throughout the western territories. Sky King was a stunt pilot with six guns. However, my favorite serial hero wasn't even a person, but rather was a horse. This wasn't your everyday garden-variety equine character though. This horse was *Pinto the Wonder Horse,* who was not only as fast as the wind but was also as smart as Einstein. Pinto could do math!

An old song by Tom T. Hall, one of America's all-time best country singers in the history of music, tells the story of Pinto the Wonder Horse best when he sings the following lyrics, *Oh we rode the dusty trails together, at the Saturday morning picture show.* The lyrics then went on to state, *We believed that Pinto was the fastest horse alive. If he outran the wind itself, we never were surprised.* And so on and so forth about the great and mythical Pinto.

Pinto was smart and could count to five, which was better than what some of my friends could do. This miraculous fact was demonstrated every week, at the beginning of that week's serial episode at the Saturday morning picture show. How this worked was that there was a sort of handler who personally led Pinto through his trick to make sure that everything went smoothly. First the handler would introduce Pinto to the audience, which was pretty much a theatre full of pre-adolescent boys. Girls didn't seem to be interested in getting up early to see *some silly old cowboys and Indians shooting at each other.* As far as us boys went, twelve years old was a popular age for the Saturday morning picture show. Pretty much every twelve-year-old boy in town would be there.

Pinto's handler, a Cowboy Pete, would hold forth at great length about how very smart Pinto was and how he had *learnt* to count while still a young pony. Cowboy Pete would then gather himself up, look Pinto directly in the eye, and say, with some ceremony, "Pinto, please count to five!" He would then give Pinto a slice of apple while giving the audience a big wink as if to say, "We're all in this together."

Pinto would get a sort of faraway, thoughtful look in his eyes, and after a few false starts and being fed a few more apples slices to stimulate his intellect, Pinto would begin to slowly and methodically clop his right front foot up and down on the floor of the movie studio, which was somewhere in Hollywood, which was somewhere in California. Every week when Pinto got up to five clops, the camera would suddenly veer away from him and back on Cowboy Pete, who had by now moved to another area of the studio. Cowboy Pete always had the same look of utter amazement on his face, as he waxed rhapsodic about the amazing level of Pinto's intelligence. Each and every twelve-year-old boy in the audience would give a sharp intake of breath and a believing sigh when Pinto reached five clops, and then stopped. At least we assumed he stopped, since the camera went away to another part of the studio.

However, there was one fateful day at the Saturday morning picture show when the usual cameraman had come down with the howling skitters and had to stay home from work. I don't believe the substitute cameraman was fully informed concerning some of the specific details of the filming of Pinto's amazing counting trick. And so it was that, just as Pinto got up to the usual five clops, at the moment that the camera would always veer away from Pinto and back on to Cowboy Pete, the substitute cameraman did not, in fact, veer the camera away. Thusly, we were all exposed to seeing Pinto continue to clop his right front foot up and down, up and down, for a dozen or more times. Dreamily munching on his apple while thinking his own private Pinto thoughts. All of a sudden the camera was jerkily taken off of Pinto. There were some muffled cursing and scuffling sounds as the camera was temporarily shut off and a brief commercial for birth control products was shown.

We were all confused and very concerned about how Pinto could have gotten so mixed up about his counting, which was always so spot on with regard to his accuracy. We also did not understand the commercial about birth control. What was a Trojan ultra-thin? In just a few moments, Cowboy Pete, with a big reassuring smile, was back in front of the camera and Pinto was nowhere to be seen. He seemed ruffled and distracted as he explained that Pinto had suffered a small horse stroke, which messed up his counting. He went on to reassure us that Pinto would be fully recovered by the next week. We were also told that the regular cameraman would be back by then as well. Cowboy Pete then suggested that we not mention anything to our moms about the commercial mix-up, which was supposed to be about bicycles.

Before anything further could go wrong, the serial was continued from where it had left off the previous Saturday. Pinto was still chasing down the bank robbers while undoubtedly solving some complicated algebra problem in his noble head. Then the main feature came on and we were all suddenly staring at a Roy Rogers movie, something titled *Roy Rogers and the Outlaws of Rustler's Canyon.* There was still an undercurrent of twelve-year-old murmuring going on in the theatre as we all tried to absorb what had happened to Pinto the Wonder Horse when he had his little horse stroke. We also wondered what the word *Trojan* meant. Was that like the Trojan horse that we had studied about in history class?

Now we fast-forward exactly ten years to the time of my being thrown off of, dragged through the mud by, and then stepped upon by a piece of official United States Forest Service equipment. The official identification of this equipment was as follows: *Horse, backcountry transport, with pack; name unknown.* This official bureaucratic government equipment description should have gone on to state, *Disposition surly, poor mental hygiene. Use with caution!* All this happened in California, where I was working for the summer as a seasonal Forest Ranger.

Since the area we were working in for that summer was too rough to drive into, and too far to walk to each day, and the government was too cheap, or too smart, to let us use their little helicopter, we were assigned personal horses, with serial numbers no less, as well as several pack mules for equipment transport. Since I was supposed to use this piece of U.S. Forest Service equipment for the whole summer, I decided to give him the name *Pinto Number Two.* This proved to be a big mistake within the first week of the summer. This horse was not nearly as smart as the original Pinto The Wonder Horse, although this horse seemed to be counting the many ways he was trying to injure me, possibly for life.

Pinto Number Two was not the fastest horse alive, and he certainly could not outrun the wind. In fact, he could not even outrun his own clumsy big feet, which he was constantly tripping over. His natural horse IQ was probably about the same as his age, which was twelve. He was also a very ill-tempered horse, in addition to being as dumb as a box of rocks.

And so it came to pass that our crew was working in the Lost Meadows Valley, which was a very long horseback ride that could have been a very comfortable twenty-minute helicopter ride, if the United States Forest Service wasn't so stingy and if any one of us had even the slightest idea of how to operate a small helicopter. During the day in question, *Pinto Number Two* was tired and out of sorts by nine o'clock and was working up to being in a very bad mood. As a result of gulping in a big belly full of air while I was trying to saddle him, he also suffered from excessive flatulence, which caused the two of us to have to remain at the rear of the column.

We were just coming down a fairly steep trail as we entered into Lost Meadows when the heroic and brave *Pinto Number Two* saw a stick that might possibly have looked like a serpent if you really stretched your imagination to the breaking point. If *Pinto Number Two* could use words, he would have screamed, "SNAKE!" right before he bolted directly out from under the saddle that I was comfortably sitting upon.

As I mentioned, when I was saddling him earlier that morning, he had taken in a huge gut-load of empty air so that the belly straps of the saddle wouldn't be too tight for his personal comfort and convenience. Pretty much all of that air had been released during the ride out, in the form of enough flatulence to float the Hindenburg dirigible. As a result, the saddle had become loose enough to slide down and nearly off his back end when he bolted for his life, away from the deadly poisonous stick.

As I slid off of his back end, my boot heel got caught in the stirrup and I found myself being dragged alongside the noble *Pinto Number Two*, who was running for his life from a smallish piece of forest debris. Unfortunately, the stick snake had gotten caught up in the mess he was dragging at high speed down the trail into the marshy Lost Meadows. *Pinto Number Two* couldn't take his one good eye off of that vicious stick that seemed to be chasing him. It was fortunate for me that the ground was wet and grassy instead of dry and rocky.

Eventually then saddle became completely detached from this deranged beast and I was able to sit up and begin regaining my greatly reduced composure. Unfortunately, however, it was at that time that *Pinto Number Two* decided to kill the stick snake, which had gotten shoved up my pants leg. While I was still on the ground, he began to clop his right front foot up and down upon the stick snake, and upon my leg. He clomped exactly five times, very much like the real *Pinto The Wonder Horse* used to do at the Saturday morning picture show. I was finally able to get the stick snake out of my Levis and throw it over my shoulder and back up the trail, where it had been lurking in its nest, waiting for its next victim, when we rode by earlier.

It took *Pinto Number Two* most of the morning to recover from his traumatic encounter with the dreaded stick snake. When I saddled him later that afternoon for the ride back to our base camp, I threatened to beat him about the head and shoulders with a much larger stick snake if he pulled that air-in-the-belly trick again. He merely rolled his eyes, clopped his right front foot threateningly at me, and fartulated loudly, exactly five times.

Teaching Bridge at the
Water Canyon Roadhouse and Stables

I ONCE SPENT SEVERAL MONTHS TEACHING a stable of whores how to play bridge. This unique happenstance occurred while I was a Ranger/Timber Cruiser working for the US Forest Service on the Cibola National Forest, which was about an hour south of Albuquerque in the state of New Mexico, also known as the land of enchantment. As a government employee, I had some extra time on my hands.

Immediately previous to this New Mexico posting, I was a Lookout Tower Ranger on the Kaniksu National Forest, on the far northern boundary of America between the state of Washington and British Columbia. Most willingly I descended from Timber Mountain after fourteen weeks of not seeing another living person except the helicopter pilot who brought my supplies twice a month. This was a lady-type helicopter pilot, and I had managed to develop a huge crush on her over the course of the summer. But then, as I recall, I also had a big crush on a lady moose that scavenged around the base of the tower during the evening hours. I was in an inter-species kind of romantic mood.

And so it came to pass that I was finally brought down from upon Timber Mountain. I was then taken to the little logging town of Usk to be debriefed and acclimatized after being in a sort of solitary confinement for three and a half months. There was female companionship in Usk in the form of the daughter of Julian Lacoste, the very colorful French Canadian bullcook at the Usk Lumber Camp. Her enchanting name was Altagracia Lacoste. But then any woman's name would have enchanted me at that point as I was in a romantic state of mind and body. I still have a sweatshirt of Altagracia's that she removed from her personal chest and gave to me, which says *Lacoste* on it.

Altagracia wanted to know what it was like being alone for fourteen weeks. I was moved to demonstrate how strongly I felt about it. And this is how I was sweetly reacquainted with civilization during that time spent waiting for the train to Albuquerque. I often wondered if the lovely Ms. Lacoste might have been a part of some sort of US Forest Service-sponsored *Compassionate Companionship* program meant to revive the libidos of returning single, young lookout tower operators.

Later in the week, after Altagracia had her wanton way with me yet again, the Ranger shuttle dropped me off at the train station in Spokane with all my worldly possessions stuffed down into my USMC duffle bag. I also had a Winchester 30-30 lever-action carbine, which I was allowed to have on the lookout as a bear deterrent. I didn't know if there were bears in New Mexico but I felt, what the hail, better safe than sorry. These days, in the year of our Lord 2012, it is difficult to comprehend being allowed on a train carrying a 30-30 lever-action carbine, but no one seemed to take special notice back then.

Once I arrived in Albuquerque, I took the Greyhound to Socorro, which was about seventy-five miles due south and the headquarters of the Cibola National Forest. If all worked as planned, I would find a place to sleep that night and from there, I would make my way to the Magdalena Ranger Station to report in by 8:00 the next morning. The travel plans were sketchy on this last leg of the trip as there was no bus, or any other form of public transportation, that could be depended on to take me the twenty-five miles from Socorro to Magdalena, pop. 1,000 lively souls.

When I climbed down from the Albuquerque bus at the Socorro Greyhound station, it was around 9:00 in the evening and I hadn't eaten anything since my early breakfast, prepared by Julian Lacoste as a friendly going-away gesture. I was exhausted from Altagracia's recent attentions, as well as very hungry, and I had no idea what people in this part of the country ate.

But this is where my New Mexico adventure officially began, for right next door to the bus station was Rosa's Cantina, a very authentic-looking Mexican restaurant. They were just getting ready to close up when I opened their door, dragging my duffle bag behind me. I must have looked pretty hungry and lost because they agreed to fix me a plate of food if I knew what I wanted. I explained, in my thick southern drawl, that I had never eaten Spanish food before and didn't understand it. I would be happy to just have two or three grilled cheese sandwiches and maybe some shrimps and grits, if that was okay. The first thing the waitress Carmelita said was, "You aren't from around here are you?" I explained that I was just down from a lookout tower up on the Canadian border and was going to the Magdalena Ranger Station in the morning, if I could find a way to get there.

I was told that they did not serve grilled cheese sandwiches, or grits or any other gringo food, but they would fix me a *Grande* plate of their house specials if I promised to try everything they cooked for me. The total cost, including a chilled *cervesa,* whatever that was, would be $4.00. I said, "Y'all go on and bring that Spanish food and I'll try it all." By the time I'd finished my first *cervesa,* which I discovered was the word they used for beer, the *Grande Especialle* platter of exotic steaming delights arrived with another of the *cervesas.* I clearly recall thinking that this was some of the best food I had ever placed upon my palate. There were numerous items on the gigantic platter including at least two beef tacos, a cheese enchilada, a chile relleno, a pork tamale, several large scoops of rice and more scoops of beans, as well as a container of steamed tortillas.

I ate my way completely through that entire platter of excellent Spanish food and was well into my third *cervesa,* and getting plenty drowsy, when I began to wonder where I was going to throw my sleeping bag down for the night. I also wondered how I was going to get to the Magdalena Ranger Station by 8:00 the next morning. Luckily, while I ate I had been sitting and talking with Carmelita, who I learned was Rosa's daughter, so I explained my situation to her. Her family talked among themselves in a language unknown to me and agreed to let me sleep in the back of the diner if I didn't shoot anyone with the *buffalo gun.*

Carmelita also suggested that if I was up by 5:45, when the restaurant began opening for breakfast, she would cook me some *muy deliciasio huevos rancheros.* Then I could ride to Magdalena with the milk route truck, which would be by promptly at 6:30 to make the daily delivery.

The first thing the milk route driver, whose name was *Hose A* said when I greeted him in my native drawl the next morning was, "You're not from around here are you?"

Hose A was a veteran of giving the lost and forlorn rides from Socorro into Magdalena and refused to accept any payment for the favor. However, I did get to help him and his co-worker, *Wan,* unload a delivery at the only stop along the way. This stop was at the *Water Canyon Roadhouse and Stables. Hose A* gave me the short and colorful version of what Water Canyon was all about. My interest was aroused and I decided to find out more for myself, at the first chance that came along.

I arrived at the Ranger Station at 7:45 and by 8:00 was checked in as being on time and fit for work. I was assigned housing in an apartment directly over the stable at the rear of the station and told that when I was *in town,* I would be living there. However, most of my time during the workweek would be spent out at the high country camp up in the Mesa Del Oro section of the Gallinas Mountains, which was a part of the larger Sangre De Cristo mountain range. I asked what Sangre De Cristo meant and was told *Blood of Christ.* I thought that was some very pretty Spanish talk.

I was given the rest of the morning to get organized and go down to the general store to buy some new work boots and a blanket-lined Levi jacket, which I would need for the cold fall weather that was on the way. At noon I was introduced to the two memorable characters who made up the rest of my crew for the next four months. The older of these two was a crusty curmudgeon by the name of Tuffy Swopp. He seemed to be in charge as he was in his mid-fifties and had *several years of high school under his belt.* He went on to say that he had almost graduated, by accident, when they had mixed him up with his cousin Buffy Swopp, but the mistake had been discovered.

His partner was a lanky character by the name of Tom Payne who was in his mid-forties and had gone *right through the sixth grade without stopping* before he had to quit to work on his family's ranch. These two *cowbums* had worked together for years and spent a great deal of time trying to decide who was in charge. When they learned that, actually, I would be in charge, they seemed greatly relieved, although both referred to me as *the college kid* for the duration of the season.

Tuffy Swopp was the camp cook and overall organizer of their usual weeks out in the high country while Tom took care of the livestock, which consisted of two mules and three horses. Tom also drove the stock truck so Tuffy could drink comfortably. Tuffy had earned a ferocious stomach ulcer from years of courting the squaws at the nearby Navajo Indian Reservation and eating their very spicy food. He also was a lifelong heavy drinker, which didn't help the condition of his already compromised stomach. His doctor forbade him from drinking any form of alcohol and had recently put him on a strict milk diet until his condition improved. Unfortunately, Tuffy had almost no use for milk and felt strongly that it was not intended to be consumed by humans but rather, to be used as calf food.

Tuffy Swopp had a countywide reputation as a *rounder and a bounder* and spent most of his energies planning and plotting how he was going to *slip up* on some cute little squaw, or her sister, or her mother, or maybe even her grandmother, if she was slow. The first day we met, Tuffy grumbled to me that he was missing his good lizard boots because they were still under Maria Gonzales' bed. He had to leave them there the previous evening when her husband, Hector Gonzales, came home earlier than expected from the local rodeo. Tuffy had gone out the back bedroom window barefoot and had to walk three miles back to town in his socks since Maria was unavailable to give him a ride to his truck.

On the other hand, Tom Payne was a much more mild and understated individual who resembled Ichabod Crane in *The Legend of Sleepy Hollow*. He was very shy and unassuming in most ways, except on Saturday night when, according to himself, he became a *sexy beast*. Tom was also a drinker but he had a strong craving for Coors Beer, which he called Colorado Kool-Aid. Both of these characters drove wrecked old dust-covered pickup trucks that looked very similar to each other. Either one of the trucks could have been in a major wreck without there being any noticeable change in its overall appearance. They said their trucks were *from the same litter.* I quickly learned how to tell their trucks apart because the back of Tom's old truck was always filled with empty Coors cans. You could hear him coming from miles away as he drove over the rutted dirt roads with his collection of tin cans. He referred to them as *road cokes* and on the weekend he was never without one clenched between his legs as he drove from one watering hole to the next.

We developed a comfortable pattern over the following four months as we worked together. On Monday morning, we would meet at the Ranger Station, where I bunked on the weekends, and get the horses and pack mules loaded up while Tom checked out and gassed up a truck and stock trailer for us to use that week.

While he was doing that, Tuffy and I walked across the road to the grocery store and bought our supplies for the week. This included several largish bottles of Jim Beam for Tuffy and several cases of Coors Beer for Tom. They had little interest in anything else at the store so it was up to me to see that we had food for the week, although Tuffy would compromise and buy one quart of milk, which he planned to drink on our two-hour drive up into the Gallatin Mountains.

We wouldn't be more than two miles out of town on our early Monday morning departure before Tuffy would reach behind the seat and pull out a pint of Jim Beam. He would balance it carefully in his lap while he opened the only quart of milk we had for the week and poured half of it out the window. He would then refill the glass milk jar up to the top with the Jim Beam and nurse that devil's mixture throughout the drive out to work. He said that this was necessary for the general health of his stomach and what the Doctor had recently prescribed for him.

When we reached the high country camp, a ramshackle bunkhouse, cook shack and split rail corral arrangement left over from the early Roosevelt administration, Tom would pen up the horses and mules and then take the trailer off the truck while I unloaded the supplies and groceries for the week. While this industry was going on, Tuffy would head directly inside saying he planned to *do some work around the bunkhouse.* Once inside he would find his way to his bunk, lay out his sleeping bag, remove his boots and lapse into a deep slumber for the rest of the afternoon. He could always be depended upon to be up in time to cook us dinner while having his evening *toddy*. No work was ever accomplished on Monday, as it was considered a travel and camp set-up day.

Tuffy Swopp was the camp cook because of his biscuit-making abilities. Our diet for the week, every week, was some narrow variation on the basic building blocks of biscuits, bacon, and beans. Three times each day, every day. Tuffy made very good biscuits and had actually won some sort of local contest once upon a time. He said the secret was his use of *bacon butter*. The biscuits, bacon, and beans menu was occasionally made even more exciting by throwing some venison or antelope meat, and on one occasion, bear meat into the bean pot. In any case, nothing green ever entered either of their personal alimentary canals. That would be unheard of and possibly harmful. And then there was the coffee. A big pot of strong black coffee was cooking on the wood stove at all times of the day and night. No sugar. No cream. No mocha latte. Just rivers of strong black coffee.

Tuffy had a saying that he liked to bring up whenever I complained about the constant diet of biscuits and beans: "When you've been eating biscuits and beans for so long that you can't stand it any more, even a change to beans and biscuits can be a relief."

As might be expected, the constant diet of beans played havoc with the air quality within the bunkhouse so we spent most nights with the door and windows wide open to the fresh mountain air. When I brought up the possibility of critters coming in while we slept, both were very surprised at my concern. As Tom put it, he "couldn't imagine a varmint dumb enough to come into a place that smells this durn bad with so much snoring and grunting and farting going on all night long."

At the end of our first week of working together, after we had arrived back in Magdalena and put away the livestock and returned the truck to the motor pool, Tom asked if I might want to go eat tacos. I fondly recalled Rosa's Cantina in Socorro and replied, "Yes, I would like a tacos." Tom and I walked several blocks down from the ranger station and came upon *Montoya's Mexican Grill and Taco Emporium*, a very small diner set-up with three tables and a dozen or so mismatched chairs. Although the place was empty, there was a jukebox and numerous beer signs on the walls. This was encouraging.

As we entered, a burly fellow in his mid-thirties pushed through the swinging door from the kitchen and greeted Tom with pleasure. Tom introduced me to Trigger Montoya as *Ranger Dave from South Carolina.* Tom explained that I would be around until the end of the year when I would be leaving to go back to college. He mentioned that I was working with himself and Tuffy Swopp. Trigger groaned at the mention of Tuffy and asked Tom to have him stop by that weekend and settle up his beer and taco bill for the past month.

Trigger was the kind of person who is instantly likeable. He brought us *cervesas* and joined us for a few minutes while he was waiting for some magic to occur back in the kitchen. Something was heating up and getting ready to be converted into tacos. The beers were fifty cents per bottle, and he only served Mexican *cervesas*–Modelo, Tecate, and Pacifico–so Tom had to forgo his usual Coors. Over the months I developed a strong affection for Negra Modelo which was the thicker, darker, stronger sub-species of Modelo, and quite tasty.

After making some small talk and listening to a provocative sizzling sound coming from the kitchen, Trigger went back there and fussed around for a few minutes. He then came out with a platter of tacos and bowls of beans and rice. We had not ordered our food yet, but this choice must have been what Trigger figured we needed at that time. All three of us ate tacos and drank beers as Trigger brought us up to date on the happenings in Magdalena while we had been up in the high country for the past week. Trigger called it the *who shot Juan* news report, as it seemed few weeks would go by without someone shooting someone else, either over a woman or a pickup truck, or both.

The tacos, priced two for a dollar, were delicious. That's the only way they were sold and you invited a heaping of scorn if you should mistakenly order just a single taco. If you did, you still paid a dollar.

Trigger didn't like to make change. The way it worked at Montoya's Mexican Grill and Taco Emporium was the customer came in and said the word *tacos,* and everything else was predetermined. Within a mere five minutes two tacos on a plate with rice and beans would appear at your table. This simple process worked for all the "regulars," which I became after that first night. I would guess that I ate no fewer than two hundred of Trigger's excellent tacos during my four months at the Magdalena Ranger Station. Trigger's tacos tasted especially good after a weeklong diet of biscuits, bacon, and beans.

Trigger and I got along famously, and I grew accustomed to showing up whenever we got back into town. The routine was always the same: two tacos and two Negra Modelos while sitting at a little table back in the kitchen watching Trigger perform his taco act at the big gas grill. We had both been in the Marine Corps for a brief stint, and we enjoyed talking about our boot camp experience and all the things that occurred afterward.

As we were leaving Trigger's after that first visit, Tom mentioned that he was going to make his weekly trip to the Water Canyon Roadhouse and Stables the next evening, as he did every Saturday. I was invited to go along if I was *of a mind to.* Tom said that he had some friends there that I might like to meet. Since I had no transportation on the weekends, and nowhere to go if I did, I said sure, I would like to tag along. Little did I know what role this colorful roadside business would play in my life during the four months I worked on the Cibola National Forest, while being stationed in Magdalena, New Mexico, the *Land of Enchantment.*

Saturday evening rolled around right on schedule and Tom stopped by Trigger's to pick me up along with a double order of tacos for the road. Trigger mentioned, with a wink, that I might need a little time at Water Canyon after being up on that fire tower all those months. Water Canyon was located about twelve miles east of Magdalena, which put it almost exactly halfway to Socorro. It drew customers and workers from both communities and was known as an equal opportunity employer.

When we arrived the business looked much more appealing at night than it did when I had seen it that past Monday morning as we made our milk route delivery. This business was definitely designed for the nighttime. It looked very festive with flashing red lights strung throughout the trees and over the building's wide front porch, which was cleverly covered with thousands of beer cans that had been hammered flat and nailed down. Tom proudly pointed out that many of them were Coors cans that he had personally supplied.

The parking lot was full of pickup trucks of every description, as well as several saddle ponies that were tied up to the pole railing of the porch. As we entered the double swinging doors that led directly into the well-lit interior, my heart was gladdened to see at least a dozen very attractive senoritas. The flowering daughters of New Mexico were turned out for the evening in all their finery. In fact, if truth be told, they were all dressed up like a bunch of little whores. I came to understand that the Water Canyon Roadhouse and Stables housed whores of all colors, creeds, sizes, interests, and general dispositions. In other words, it was, for lack of a better term, a genuine *whorehouse*. Little did I appreciate how well I would get to know each and every member of that happy little band of whores over the period of the next four months. Even better, most of them were card-playing whores.

Tom took me around to each and every little whore and introduced me as *Ranger Dave from South Carolina*, again explaining that I would be working with himself and Tuffy Swopp for the next four months. One of the little whores got that special look that often occurred when Tuffy's name was mentioned. She asked Tom to have Tuffy come in sometime over the weekend and settle up his whore bill with Dora. After that evening, whenever one whore introduced me to another whore I hadn't met yet, whore #1 would say something like, "Trixie, you little whore, this is Ranger Dave. He talks funny because he's not from around here." The whores of Water Canyon were a very refined and proper bunch when it came to manners and etiquette.

Tom finished off the round of introductions by taking me up to the bar and introducing me to Joe Delicious, the one and only bartender at the Water Canyon Roadhouse and Stables. Tom said he "could be moody if it was his time of month." I smiled warmly and said that I would like to have "a nice Chardonnay," since it was a warm day and that sounded refreshing to me. Joe Delicious became somewhat agitated and moody and said in a no-nonsense voice, "We have beer and whiskey, no wine. No Merlots, no Burgundies, and certainly no *nice* Chardonnays. Nothin' made out of grapes." I was feeling obnoxious and couldn't help but say, "Okay then, how about a nice Pinot Noir?" Joe left in a huff to go wait on a more cooperative customer who wanted a *CC & Seven*. Joe Delicious and I never did hit it off so well.

Over the course of the first several weeks of visiting Water Canyon, I learned the whores were kept extremely busy on Friday and Saturday nights; but on Sunday nights when most of their customers were busy doing church-related activities, they were downright bored. My main interest was in hanging out with the little whores, getting to know them, and having a Negra Modelo or two while listening to all of their outrageous stories of adventures in the whore business. I thought I might even write a story about all that someday. The girls were very comfortable being referred to as whores and constantly referred to themselves in the same vernacular, as in, "Flopsy, you little whore, would you be so kind as to fetch me a chilled glass to go with this lovely Modelo that Ranger Dave has purchased for me?"

The girls were always looking for games and non-business-related activities to entertain themselves during the slow Sunday evenings.

I studied their unsuccessful attempts to play poker and suspected just the name of the game, *poker,* was too close to being business-related for them to enjoy. Therefore, I decided to have a Sunday evening talk about cards with Dora and Flora. They were sisters and recognized as the *bull whores* in this establishment. Bull whores did not mean they were from the Isle of Lesbos but rather gave them the distinction of being the alpha whores among the group.

I bought us a round of beers and we sat down, whereupon I gave them their first introduction to the game of bridge. I mentioned that I had made a little money in college by playing for a penny a point. I suggested that they might consider bridge as a form of entertainment to be played on Sunday nights while all their customers were involved with church work. I explained that the game required four players to carry out the bidding process but only three players actually played the hand, as the fourth hand was known as *the dummy,* to be played by the partner who had won the bid. Flora observed that she personally knew of several dummies who worked at Water Canyon and would fit in perfectly.

I further explained that the game I would teach them had to be a special kind of bridge as the little whores were constantly joining in to play for a hand or two between customers and then disappearing through the back door to be replaced by someone who was *on break* for a few minutes. Flora and Dora agreed that the game should be named *Little Whore's Bridge.* Ultimately, I had to teach no fewer than a dozen little whores the basics of this game in order to be assured of four players at any given time. These lessons usually took place on Sunday nights, which was okay with the ladies since this time had become the established *little whore's bridge night.*

The game of *Little Whore's Bridge* caught on like wildfire throughout the Water Canyon Roadhouse and Stables. Every little whore wanted to be included. Even Big Bertha, the Boss Bull

Lady, who was actually the Madam and no longer active in *the pro-fession*, wanted to learn how to play. Big Bertha accused me of coming from out of town and *trying to refine her little whores*. She went on to say "The next thing you know, they'll be trying to establish a Little Whore's Union, or some other communist plot!"

Big Bertha was fond of saying of my efforts, "You can lead a horticulture, but you can't make her think."

Recent archeological dig in New Mexico reveals the remains of the stables portion of the Water Canyon Roadhouse and Stables. Photo taken circa 2007.

PART THREE

HOW SHARPER THAN A SERPENT'S TOOTH, CONCERNING THE FINEST DAUGHTER IN ALL THE LAND

Little Miss Awesome Face at two years and already a mighty hunter. Just outside of the photo frame is a fully-grown Guernsey cow that had caught Savannah's attention. She holds out a cow cookie with the intent of luring the unsuspecting bovine into range so she can attack it with her sharp little milk teeth. Note slight rivulet of drool as she imagines how many steaks this cow might contain.

Savannah's Favorite Animal Is the Steak

WHEN MY DAUGHTER SAVANNAH A. KILBOURNE, the finest daughter in all the land, was in kindergarten, the class was asked to share what their favorite animal was. Savannah's teacher, Mrs. Montgomery, Savannah's BFF teacher for ever and ever, later told me that while most of the kids quickly answered in favor of puppies, kitties, horsies, butterflies, rainbows or unicorns, Savannah answered with some conviction that her favorite animal was the steak.

After hearing Mrs. Montgomery's amused report, I was so proud of Savannah, the finest daughter in all the land, that I was moved to write a poem in honor of her sixth birthday, as well as in recognition of her particular culinary preferences. The little ditty goes something like this:

Beef, A Love Story

I loves beefs! I loves the flank and I loves the shank.
I loves briskets on triscuits with gravy and biscuits.
I chill it then grill it upon a hot skillet.
Beef pudding pie is what I make. My favorite animal is the steak.
Broil it, steam it, toast it, stew it. Shish-ka-bob or barbecue it.
I stir fry and pan fry, I braise and I broast.
Whereupon I rewards me tummy with a fine pot roast.
Gimme a half cow or just a mere haunch,
bottom, top, left, right, mornings, evenings, day, or night
Back ribs … Front ribs … Baby ribs … Bully ribs.
On any kind of ribs, I got the dibs.
Gimme that beef. Gimme that juicy steak device.
Gimme that beefcake for dessert. So sweet and extra nice.
Beefs loves me!

"Dedicated to my carnivorous little daughter, Savannah, the finest daughter in all the land. So Happy Birthday already. Now let's go out and eat some steak!"

Well, I admit openly and without shame that in this case, the little carnivore is living up to this parental unit's own preferences, although I have to say for the record that my favorite animal has always been the one that tastes the best, which in my case is the ever wily southern pulled pork. However, enough said on that delicious topic as my obsession with the pig and all its tasty parts is described in great detail elsewhere in this collection.

My second favorite animal is the Pool Hall Chili Dog prepared and sold only at City Billiards, located at 208 Richland Avenue in lovely Aiken, South Carolina. This foodstuff was at the top of my feeding chain during my formative years while attending Aiken High School. The dogs are boiled senseless, the fluffy buns are steamed into a cloud-like consistency, and the chili is made of ... well, no one seems to know exactly. The original recipe came from a worthy by the name of Casto Golden (his real name, I swear!). He was Corsican, or something like that.

As far as I can tell, the big iron chili pot at the back of the crusty stove has not been moved, or emptied, since day one. Every day upon closing, a new batch of ingredients is simply added to what was left in the pot from that day's business. Local mythology has it that the substance at the bottom of the pot hasn't seen the light of day since the Eisenhower Administration. It does have a certain mature flavor. It is also the best chili ever created!

Our late Quasar Microwave that lived in the pantry. Seen in this photo after heating its last meal. Note steaming blown-open can of Chef Boyardee Wheat Flavored Lasagna In Hearty Tomato-Like Sauce steaming like Old Faithful Geyser in Yellowstone National Park. "Self-opening" lid to can was found embedded in wall on far side of pantry. Note bottle of Love Potion No. 69 Strong Ale on top of microwave. Most useful for putting out small fires, especially in the stomach.

My Daughter Likes to Blow Things Up

*I*T WAS A COLD AND RAINY AFTERNOON. *The wind howled into the garage. I stood there shivering with a blowtorch in one hand and a piece of old silk skirt in the other. After applying the flamethrower to the silk, a complete conflagration occurred. The fabric burned with some vigor. My Daddy said I had to move out of the garage or I might blow up his home brewing laboratory.*

That little bit of dramatic narrative was directly quoted from my daughter Savannah's *8th Grade Science Fair Experiment Report* that was set up to determine which fabrics burned more readily than others. Even though it is common knowledge that Savannah A. Kilbourne is the finest daughter in all the land, at times her *scientific experiments* can be frightening, or even distasteful, as is demonstrated by the following cake-baking experiment.

In this infamous 7th Grade Science Fair project, Savannah was to cook five one-layer cakes, with each cake missing a different necessary ingredient. The five necessary ingredients involved were flour, sugar, eggs, milk and, of course, bacon.

The taste and texture of each cake was then to be described in a written narrative. Only scientific terms were to be used in the report. Terms such as *yucky* and *barf-like* were not considered scientific.

An excellent example of the dark side of pure scientific research occurred with *the dreaded mixture #5,* which had the flour eliminated. When baked, the resultant substance resembled an undercooked puddle of buffalo yuck, although not as pretty. I had foolishly agreed to taste each cake with Savannah, and I will never forget the scientific sliminess and noxiousness of *the dreaded #5.* Savannah wanted to adopt a new scientific measurement to best describe the horrible taste, such as, *this mixture registered a solid seven on the Kilbourne Putridity Scale.*

I urged her to consider dropping out of her science class rather than have to taste that cake, but she said the course wasn't an elective. The only thing that saved the cake was the bacon.

Then there was the *incident* when Savannah decided to cook her own dinner. I had stepped next door to help our neighbor lady move a heavy piece of furniture and was unaware of Savannah's plan to explode our kitchen in my brief absence.

When I came back twenty minutes later, I found Savannah watching her favorite *Discovery Channel* program, *Blowing Things Up*, while addressing a steaming bowl of canned lasagna. I was pleasantly surprised and asked if she had cooked that up all by herself. I recall saying, "So you successfully operated the can opener then?" She replied that actually the lasagna came with an automatic opening can. Confused, I asked for details, whereupon she explained that she had put the can in the microwave for three minutes and could tell when it was ready because she could hear the can open from all the way in the living room, with the TV on. She mentioned that some tomato sauce might have spilled in the microwave when the can self-opened.

In addition to Savannah's lifelong interest in exploding things, she also has a deep abiding interest in the printed word. Now the trick is to combine these two strong interests. Her taste in literature has evolved at an alarming rate. It was just a few years ago when her favorite book was *The Cat in the Hat,* and now she has just finished Douglas Adams' 800-page *Hitchhiker's Guide to the Galaxy.* She has, of course, read all of the Harry Potter books and the currently popular *Hunger Games* series. She has completed all seven of the *Artemis Fowl* books, as well as the ever-popular *Microwave Cooking with Nitroglycerine.*

While still thirteen, Savannah began exploring the literature of John Steinbeck. I don't know many kids that age who have read, and thoroughly enjoyed, *The Grapes of Wrath*. When I was that age, I was into the Hardy Boys series in which Frank and Joe Hardy and their *chums* at Bayport High solved low-level crime as a sort of hobby. Unfortunately, this would be remedial reading by Savannah's standards. After all, she uses *War and Peace* as a doorstop.

Now that Savannah is a freshman at Chico High, and is in Honors English as well as Architectural Design, I suppose something more sophisticated and exciting, like *Enlarging Your Bedroom with Explosives*, might appeal to her.

Savannah A. Kilbourne. The finest daughter in all the land as she casts reproachful look over left shoulder. Her look is saying, "How could you possibly deny this angelic face a little Canny right now?" Note coy placement of left foot to further emphasize canny-worthy "cuteness factor." String secured to left wrist is attached to a balloon, which proclaims, "Hershey's products are good for you! Eat more Canny today!"

Miss Awesome Face

MY DAUGHTER, SAVANNAH A. KILBOURNE, the finest daughter in all the land, was an outspoken child at four years of age. Not that anything has changed in that regard; but it's just that when she was four, which is ten years ago now, I used to write down some of the endearing little comments that she would favor me with. Nowadays her comments aren't so endearing, and I ignore them as much as possible.

Recently I came across an envelope filled with little sticky notes upon which I used to jot down her frequent bon mots. I recall that once there was a discussion concerning what her favorite animal was. Some of her little friends said that their favorite animal was a puppy, or a kitten, or maybe a unicorn, or a horsy. However, as was mentioned in a previous story Savannah stated clearly, and with great conviction, that her favorite animal was *the steak*. My delicate little daughter was a raging carnivore.

One of her favorite words back during her days of colorful four-year-old statements was the mysterious word *canny*. Apparently *canny* was a concept that had caught her full attention, as she referred to it often. I finally asked her to tell me what she meant when she said *canny* (and then rolled her eyes deliciously). She said that she would bring me a picture. She was back shortly with a picture of a Hershey bar, with almonds. She rolled her eyes for me, and a small drop of drool escaped the corner of her delicate little bow-shaped mouth. "CANNY!" she declared with enthusiasm.

Now her previous comment that "I need a lot of canny right now!" began to make sense. She went on to explain by stating, "If I ever had to go for a whole week without canny, I would get very sick!" She followed that up with, "I can eat some canny right now if you want. Do you have any canny?"

She referred to her pillow as her *piddow* and was always losing it here or there. She would come up to me and ask, "Do you have my piddow?" I would say no, that I thought she might find it on her bed, where it was supposed to be. I discovered that the *piddow* question was just an introduction to a larger, more pressing issue, because she would then ask, "Well Daddy, since you don't have my piddow, do you maybe have some canny for me?"

Savannah was very tricky for a four-year-old. She knew that anytime she dropped the magical word *Daddy* into any request, no matter how outrageous, her chances of being successful were greatly increased. Now that she's in high school, she hasn't forgotten the magic of including the *Daddy* word in any outlandish request. Unfortunately, these days it isn't something as simple as a request for *canny*. It's more likely a request for a credit card with a high limit or a new Jacuzzi tub for her bedroom.

Now that her thirty-month orthodontics campaign has been completed, there are tens of thousands of dollars freed up to be applied to other purposes designed to enhance Savannah's general quality of life. Additionally, there will be the court costs and attorney's fees that will be incurred when she goes before the Judge to have her name legally changed. Before the braces came off she was perfectly satisfied with being referred to as Savannah A. Kilbourne, the finest daughter in all the land. That's not good enough these days. Now that we are in the post-braces stage, she insists on being called *Miss Awesome Face*. She's even having her luggage re-monogrammed!

But I digress. Back in the day when she was still known as Savannah, she was very specific about what she required for dinner and made sure I knew well in advance, so that it would be prepared for her on time. I once asked her if she wanted a hamburger, and she said that she "liked hamburgers, but only the ham part, not the burger part." Another time she said that she wanted something special for dinner that night. When I asked what she had in mind, she said that she wanted something special like "pork and cereal." I can assure you that comment activated the old gag reflex. Another evening she told me, "I would like you to cook me a whole plate of steak." I knew by then that this was her favorite animal, and she liked to eat them by the plateful.

Savannah had a fascination with sleep and sleep-related issues. She would complain when I came in to get her up for pre-school by saying, "I don't want to get my body up this soon." In the evenings she would let me know that she wasn't able to hear me when I told her it was time for her to go to bed. Her excuse was, "My ears go to sleep first and then I don't hear any more. Then my body and my heart goes to sleep." Whenever allowed, she liked to keep her body up for the late-night movies.

She was always troubled by a hand or a foot going to sleep and would say, "My foot tried to go to sleep for the night, but it was only lunchtime!" Then there was the time when she fell asleep while watching TV in the evening. She explained, "I just blinked my eyes for too long."

Savannah had issues with the concept of time. Even though I had given her a little plastic Mickey Mouse watch, she used it mainly as a decorative accessory for her tiny arm. When I would facetiously ask her what time it was, she would admit, "I can't tell time yet. I don't know if anything is a minute, an hour, or a day." She also wasn't too clear on the concept of paleontology and told many of my friends, "Daddy was born when the dinosaurs were alive. He had a long-neck dinosaur for a little pet."

She could be solicitous about my health and welfare. On several occasions, when she felt I was being overworked, she would say, "You should take a break and have a nice beer because you have been working too hard." She was also concerned about my bodily functions, and once asked during a dinner with our neighbors, "Can you tell me again about the time you had the bad diarrhea?"

One Christmas I gave Savannah a little purse without thinking ahead about what the longer-term consequences might be. She was quick to point out, "Now that I have a purse, you need to keep a dollar in it." She went on to state, invitingly, "You can also keep a little canny in it, if you want." She then rolled her big brown eyes outrageously at me.

Later that same week she mentioned, "I'm going to have to get some new moneys for my purse. I only have two moneys left." I agreed and gave her some change, which she considered to be just as valuable as paper moneys. It was all *moneys* to her. Too bad that simplistic understanding of *moneys* didn't last into her teenage years. There were some purse-related benefits to me, as she once said, "Now that I have a purse, I can take you to lunch, and we can eat some canny."

Once in a canny-deprived state of desperation, she warned me, "I will have to give you a bad spanking if you don't give me some canny!" How sharper than a serpent's tooth. These are not the words of a loving, innocent four-year-old. These are the words of a cold-blooded, dedicated canny terrorist!

The Accidental F-Bomb

I HAVE NEVER BEEN A PERSON WHO NEEDED to express himself in a profane sort of way. In fact, I have to be pushed to the limit to even utter a *hell* or a *damn,* although those words are frequently found in the Bible. You can hear a lot about those two words if you attend a certain kind of church. While I didn't come from a family that normally used profanity, I do recall my father being over-whelmed with exuberance once when describing his hole-in-one score at golf as being a *hellava shot* and a *damn fine opportunity* for his golfing buddies to buy him several congratulatory beers.

I believe one of the most over-used curse words is the one that is referred to as the *F-word* or the *F-Bomb.* It's a word that rhymes with *truck.* Even though I spent a short tour of duty in the United States Marine Corps, where cursing is as common as discussing the weather, or the ball scores, I still didn't get in the habit of using words that I couldn't use comfortably around my Sainted Mother. "Please pass the effing mashed potatoes" would be strongly frowned upon at my Sainted Mother's dinner table.

Cussing in front of the mother-person brings to mind a cute little joke that I heard somewhere, many years ago. It's one of those *Little Johnny* jokes that always features an innocent six-year-old boy who accidentally makes the most outrageous comments with-out having any understanding of what he is saying. Anyway, Little Johnny's father decided to play a joke on his wife one morning by getting his twin six-year-olds, Little Billy and Little Johnny, to say a cuss word or two at the breakfast table. The husband wanted to see what would happen and how bad it might be. He challenged the boys to somehow work the word *damn* and *hell* into a standard breakfast table comment.

When they came down that morning, their mother pleasantly asked Little Billy what he would like for breakfast. Little Billy said, "Well, what the hell, Momma, I think I'll have some of that damn oatmeal!" Little Billy's mother wound up and backhanded him so hard that he did a backover flip and then rolled up under the dining-room table. The mother then turned to Little Johnny and asked him what he might want for breakfast. He's thinking, man I got to stay away from the oatmeal, so he says, "Well, I don't know Momma, but it sure as hell isn't going to be any of that damn oatmeal!"

Even if I did have a habit of cursing in the past, like Little Johnny, I would have given that up in the year of 1997, for this was the magical time when a brand spanking new daughter arrived on the scene. Savannah had tiny ears that were as fragile as pixie dust. I didn't want her to ever experience even a *darn* or a *heck*. Her little ears were made out of pure spun angel's fluff and cherub's breath and were so virginal and pure that I constantly monitored each and every sound that might find its way down into her delicate little ear sockets.

However, there was the one event that will always remain painfully clear in my mind as the regretful time I dropped the *F-Bomb*, totally by accident. I was driving from somewhere to somewhere else, deep in thought, when this wreck of a pickup truck, with a busted muffler and an extra-loud radio, suddenly pulled across in front of me, so close that it almost brushed my front bumper. I had to slam on my brakes to keep from T-boning it amidships. I responded emotionally, without thinking, with that primitive part of the brain that cusses. I deeply regret that I shouted the *F-word*, as in *F**K!!* very loudly, and with double exclamation marks, but without the little asterisks.

As soon as that BIG word jumped out of my mouth and was still ringing in the air of our little enclosed car, confined inside the car because it was winter and all the windows were rolled up, and the word couldn't get out, a severe sinking sense of dread overtook me. Probably not since the sinking of the battleship Maine, in the

Havana harbor, immediately prior to the kick-off of the Spanish-American War, had I had such an acute sinking feeling. My feeling was that dreadful and that filled with foreboding.

I kept thinking, what is it? What is it that is causing me to have this sinking feeling that something terribly, horribly wrong has just occurred? And just at that moment, I heard this teensy, tiny little voice coming from the back seat. A voice that was so tiny that it still had to be kept in a little voice booster seat. The tiny fragile voice asked, "Daddy, what did you say?" I had the original *OMG!!* moment right then and there when I realized Savannah had been quietly riding around in the back seat. So quiet. So very quiet. Quiet as an innocent little mousy with virginal ears made of spun angel's wings.

She liked to sit back there and just blend in with the upholstery while she stared out at the world through the innocence of three-year-old eyes. She was probably looking for butterflies or rainbows or maybe unicorns. She could be so very quiet that I would forget that she was back there until we arrived at wherever we were driving to. I had completely forgotten that she was riding with me and that gigantic, four-gigahertz *F-Bomb* was still loudly bouncing all around inside the car, off the radio knobs and into the rearview mirror and then into the heater controls. Apparently it had even ricocheted into the rear passenger area!

I carefully said, "Oh, that. Well, that big ugly truck over there almost ran us off the road and I shouted, TRUCK!! at it. That's all. That's all I shouted. I didn't shout anything else!" She said in a tiny, lower-case voice, "oh." I was desperate to change the subject and I asked her, "So, how are things going back there, anyway?" She thought about this for a few seconds, and then said, "Daddy, my tummy needs a little canny right now." We stopped at the next canny store, and that was the end of the accidental *F-Bomb* incident.

Overbooking dilemma! Books overflowing onto windowsill cause view of outside world to be blocked and natural light to be interrupted. A few of the 3,280 titles in the library. Do you see one you might want to borrow? You understand the overdue fine, right?

A Book Report Measured by the Linear Foot

I LIKE TO READ. No, that's not quite right. That's sort of like saying, I like to breathe. I *have* to read. Although I've been an avid reader for quite a few years now, I understand I still have a lot of books to read yet if I plan to read them all. I know this since I've just seen a study, which concluded that there are 3.1 million individual titles in print worldwide. How many actual total books currently exist will never be known. However, I know exactly where 3,280 of them are, because they are right here in our home library.

How do I know this seemingly random number, you may ask. Let me explain. I read recently on this nifty website, *Omnivoracious,* that the best way to determine how many books you have in your home library is to literally, so to speak, measure them. My daughter, Savannah A. Kilbourne, the finest daughter in all the land, and another avid reader (this may be an inherited trait) got right on the job by taking her little pink measuring tape in hand and measuring the length of all the bookshelves in our home. Although dusty and exhausted, she soldiered on and eventually returned with a page full of calculations, to report that the total was 328 linear feet of bookshelves. This vast measurement included slightly less than one foot of self-help books and cookbooks. Enough said on that issue.

As dedicated book engineers, we then, again using the little pink measuring tape, took several sample counts of how many books would fit in one linear foot. The answer was an average of ten. For your own measurement purposes, it should be noted that our book collection is 90 percent hardbound and the rest paperback, although not the smaller trade paperback format. We eschew those. We then multiplied the overall bookshelf length by ten to get the total number of books in our home library which ended up being precisely 3,280, give or take a hundred or two.

You might ask, who writes these books and what are they about? The subject matter ranges from American classics such as the works of Steinbeck, Hemingway, and Fitzgerald to the books of the more contemporary writers such as T. C. Boyle, Cormac McCarthy, Hunter S. Thompson, Pat Conroy, John Krakauer, and Larry McMurtry, to name a few. The book I read last week was Wallace Stegner's *The Big Rock Candy Mountain.* As noted above, little space is dedicated to smarmy self-help books and/or tasteless cookbooks.

Of our 3,280 titles, a few of my favorites include John Steinbeck's *Cannery Row, Sweet Thursday,* and *The Grapes of Wrath,* as well as Ken Kesey's *Sometimes a Great Notion. The Stand,* which is one of Stephen King's earliest works is also a favorite title. I had the pleasure of joining himself for a beer (I recall Sierra Nevada Pale Ale was his preference) in downtown Santa Cruz in 1994, while he was in town promoting his new book, *Insomnia,* and I was a member of the local press, with appropriate credentials, just for that afternoon. King was a tall, looming presence and seemed to fill the space of several people as he casually entered the bookstore by the back door, where he had parked his Harley-Davidson. He represented the biker look with his black leather jacket and motorcycle boots. Later, during our talking, I mentioned that his new book *Insomnia* certainly kept me awake!

I've also greatly enjoyed the books of Tom Wolfe, such as *The Electric Koolaid Acid Test* and *The Right Stuff,* and had the great pleasure of co-hosting a dinner for him one balmy Chico evening in March of 1977. He was the featured cultural *Arts 77* speaker at Chico State University that month. His *topic of discourse* was *The Blue Angel Arrives in Cultureville.* After several martinis and more discoursing, he generously agreed to sign all eight of his books in my collection, including one that was overdue from the Butte County Library. In that volume he inscribed with a great flourish,

To Dave, noted host and book purloiner, Cheers! Tom Wolfe! I sadly admit that book is still overdue.

Our home library sorting system is loosely based on the concept of organized chaos and defies all other sorting systems in the known world, including the original Dewey Decimal System introduced back in the days when Cleopatra barged the Nile. In keeping with our generous nature, and by popular demand, we operate a very active lending library for our friends and neighbors. Our policy is one book at a time with a two-week limit. After that time limit expires, the borrower is fined one bottle of Sierra Nevada Torpedo Ale per day for as long as it takes. There is no limit.

Savannah estimates that, at any given time, between two and three linear feet of books are checked out of our library. She further estimates that this number of loaned books should translate into nearly two cases of Torpedo Ale by the end of the week.

However, even with these strict rules, special privileges are granted to regular customers such as my longtime close friend, Karen Potter, a highly evolved human being who currently has three (3) overdue books checked out. Her personal idea of good reading might be exemplified by Stieg Larsson's *The Girl with the Dragon Tattoo* trilogy. Karen is in the business of selling the printed word as Editor and Publisher of *The Synthesis,* a weekly newspaper closely focused on the local pop culture and live music scene. She is a fan of John Grisham and also enjoys any books involving serial killers, psychopaths, vampires, designer shoes, or the consumption of good champagne.

Other friends have other reading tastes. For example, my lovely good friend Barbara Overhoff Geshekter, a Sensuous American, has a *highly refined* taste in books that I personally would never be able to approach, much less match. She is a very smart lady of a certain age whose elevated IQ shines through bright and clear, whether she is attending the symphony or addressing a chilled glass of good Chardonnay.

Barbara's idea of an exciting read has been spending the past year thoroughly absorbing *Love, Life, Goethe, the Biography of Wolfgang Goethe* by John Armstrong. I'm told by herself that even the paper is, and I quote, "quite sensuously orgasmic," or words to that effect. I can say honestly and without shame that Barbara seems to be getting a lot more fun out of her reading than I'm getting out of mine. The books I read are written on regular, boring paper that is not sensuous or even faintly orgasmic. I suppose I should buy better quality books to get the effect she seems to be enjoying.

My well-read daughter, Savannah A. Kilbourne, Slug Bug Champion of Georgetown County three years running, has her own specific taste in literature. She consumes books at a rate of one or two every week, or nearly one hundred annually, and is thriving in Honors English as a freshman at Chico High. She would probably characterize her favorite type of literature as fantasy fiction, such as the Harry Potter series by J. K. Rowling. She is also a big fan of Steinbeck, Tolkien, and Douglas Adams, although Leo Tolstoy not so much.

She does enjoy a bit of the Shakespeare and occasionally uses it for dramatic effect. Just the other day I overheard her on the phone with a friend who was whining about her heavy homework load. Savannah was not sympathetic and I quote her response, *Grow thou up, thou mewling beetle-headed canker blossom!* Ouch! That's got to smart!

Regarding the issue of personal preferences, within our small family of two: Although Savannah and I share many books between us such as the highly popular *Hunger Games* trilogy, currently we are not on the same page, so to speak. As previously mentioned, she enjoys fantasy-based novels and her latest find, which is a classic in the traditional battle between good and evil, is entitled *Sparkle Ponies War on the Twentieth Street Zombie Playboys.* On a different page I'm presently giving serious attention to W. Bruce Cameron's *8 Simple Rules for Dating My Teenage Daughter.* I'm going to pass on the Sparkle Ponies while she is not only disinterested in reading Cameron's very entertaining little book, she isn't interested in my reading it either. Go figure.

Savannah and I also enjoy the printed word offered in non-book format. For example, collecting bizarre and unique newspaper headlines makes for an interesting hobby. This is what refrigerator magnets were created for. Our personal all-time favorite *Onion* headline is *Heroic Pit Bull Journeys 2,000 Miles to Attack Owner.*

Actual news item describing "heroic" journey of Pit Bull Brutus as he traveled across America in determined search to find his owner, who left him behind with a two-day supply of dry Kibbles and no water, when relocating to California.

Other favorite news headlines include *Year in Jail Earned for Tearing Off Woman's Ear in Bar, Local Stoner Reports Giant Bacon Sandwich Like Totally Headed Toward Earth, Ohio Man Is Executed Despite His Protests. Cites Obesity* and the ever popular *New Zealand Man Fined for Using Hedgehog in Assault of Teen.* You just can't make this stuff up.

Well actually you can make some of it up. Whenever possible I like to (mis)quote the local daily as a useful source of propaganda now that

Savannah is nearly fifteen. For example, just the other day we were sharing a Saturday breakfast of her famous chocolate chip pancakes with jelly, jam, and maple syrup. This recipe doesn't actually require batter. I like to use these breakfast opportunities to bring her up to date on the latest news. My strategy requires that I hold the newspaper up, frowning and lightly humming to give the impression that I am pondering mightily on an item of great national interest. I'm actually reading the NFL scores, hoping to learn that the Oakland Raiders have lost again. More on them in a later story.

I then sagely comment, "Say this is interesting. It says here that recent studies indicate the number of teens having sex has dropped dramatically!" I then observe that this is certainly good news, wouldn't she agree? She rolls her eyes mightily and mentioned that I must be reading last week's paper which I mentioned reported on studies revealing that today's teens are using no drugs and are all signing contracts to remain celibate until marriage, which other current studies show isn't happening these days until most teens are into their early thirties. She then favors me with a bold eyebrow wiggle. How sharper than a serpent's tooth ….

We are also collectors of strange and unusual bumper stickers and will often contest each other to see who can spot the most interesting and creative. Savannah's favorite is *I love animals, they are delicious!* A close runner-up for her is *All I ask is that you treat me no differently than you would the Queen.* I saw one the other day that I thought was interesting. *Sexual harassment will not be tolerated; however, it will be graded.* I have given my good friend Karen Potter several stickers that should be firmly attached to her own personal bumper. Two of them are, *This is the earliest I've ever been late* and *On time means when I get there.* She is always late but worth the wait. Hey, that's another good one!

Posted notices can often be the source of entertainment. I share with you our favorite lost pet notice, recently found stapled to a utility pole in front of Camp Kilbourne, which reads as follows:

Lost dog. 3 legs, blind in left eye, missing right ear, tail broken, recently castrated. Answers to the name of Lucky. I'm sure I've seen that dog somewhere around the neighborhood.

In closing, from our *Final Wishes Archive*, I offer this worthy last wish that I came across somewhere. *When I die, I want to go peacefully, like my Grandfather did, in his sleep ... not screaming and flailing like the passengers in his car.*

PART FOUR

THE
SIERRA NEVADA BREWERY
STORIES, TOLD BACK
BY THE PIZZA OVEN

"Sierra Nevada Brewing Company is the most perfect brewery on the planet." *Michael J. Lewis, co-author of* Brewing *and Prof. Emeritus, Department of Brewing Science, University of California at Davis.*

Worshipping at The Church of the Holy Nectar

"The tavern will compare favorably with the church."
Henry David Thoreau

I PERSONALLY LIKE TO ATTEND CHURCH services at least twice a week. Sometimes more frequently if it doesn't harm my liver. I go to a *traditional* service in a big old brick church downtown on Sundays with my daughter, Savannah A. Kilbourne, the finest daughter in all the land. Additionally, every Thursday evening I go to *The Church of the Holy Nectar* services for a salutary pint, just before vespers, with my excellent longtime friend, the lovely Ms. Karen Potter. Ms. Potter is a highly evolved individual who also enjoys good champagne and expensive shoes. She has faithfully attended nearly three hundred Thursday evening services with myself over the past ten years.

The Church of the Holy Nectar is conveniently located in Chico, California at 1075 E. 20th Street and is generally open from 11:00 until 9:00 every day of the week. This very popular institution of worship is often referred to as the Sierra Nevada Taproom and Restaurant.

How can a church and a brewpub be viewed as highly similar, you ask? A famous American statesman, Founding Father and possible inventor of the holy mash tun, Dr. Benjamin *Hops* Franklin, best explained the holy connection between religion and beer when he famously stated, "Beer is living proof that God loves us and wants us to be happy." This works for me.

The Holy Trinity includes the *Pope of Sierra Nevada* whose earthly name is *His Eminence, The Most Revered Ken Grossman*. Pope Grossman is a beneficent leader of the microbrew industry and originator of The Church of the Holy Nectar, which is the largest and most successful privately owned brewchurch of its kind in America today.

At the Pope's right hand stands the beatific Steve Dresler, the *High Priest and Master Brewer of the Holy Sacrament*. At the Pope's left hand stand the two Holy Beer Encampment Dieties, also known as Counselors of the Camp, Brother Steve Grossman and Brother Terence Sullivan.

As noted, services are conveniently held seven days each week, generally from 11:00 until 9:00, except on occasional days when they are suspended to observe patriotic, pilgrim-based, and religious holidays such as Independence Day, Thanksgiving, and Christmas. One other religious holiday has special significance for The Church of the Holy Nectar, and that is Holy Fermentation Day, for this is the day that beer was officially discovered by the Phoenicians in 210 B.C. Through the astronomical study of several heavenly bodies, including those of the lovely Barbara Geshekter and the lovely Karen Potter, it has been determined that this holiday lawfully occurs on February the tenth of each odd-numbered year. Holy Fermentation Day is considered a national holiday in most micro-churches. Leap years are treated as a time of even greater joy, and all strong ales are provided to the congregation at a greatly reduced rate. Ask your server for details.

Although I myself am a mere *Regular* worshipper, I do have the honor of leading the church choir in old German drinking songs at certain times, as well as giving traditional Bavarian wedding toasts whenever appropriate. Then there are those members of the church who are considered *Superior* worshippers, such as *Brother* Sean Greer, *the Beer Evangelist*. If Brother Greer doesn't show up for worship around five o'clock of every day, he is promptly given a welfare call to verify that he is in good health.

Brother Miles Jordan, minister of the *Church of the Blues People* is another regular member of The Church of the Holy Nectar who is tasked with blessing new releases. *Brother* Steve Kasprzyk is assigned the daily feeding and handling of the reptiles and serpents while *Brother* Big Jack Roller, known to one and all down at the pub as *Holy* Roller, preaches to the choir.

As in most churches, it pays to tithe liberally at The Church of the Holy Nectar. We tithers are ecumenically assured that we will receive our just rewards at the sounding of the holy trumpet, also referred to as last call.

A thirsty gathering of The Church of the Holy Nectar Regulars. *Found in their natural habitat back by the pizza oven at the Sierra Nevada Pub during the release of the 2012 Southern Hemisphere Harvest Ale.*

We *Regulars* are a gregarious and generous group, and our tithing is rewarded with excellent service. I personally tithe regularly as well as always send Christmas cards to each of my five personal care specialists. This tasteful card discreetly contains a small piece of American currency, skillfully folded into the shape of a Christmas tree. Other worshippers might do well to follow my pious example.

These worthy Taproom caregivers previously named in the Acknowledgements section represent that special sort of Chicoan who graduated from Chico State University and elected to remain in our fair city in order to maintain a close proximity to The Church of the Holy Nectar. The Church employs the most well-educated and dedicated caregivers in all the land.

All of these gentles have a special place in my heart, for upon my arrival, during my weekly Thursday evening worship period, just before vespers, they faithfully stand ready with my holy vessel, upon which is carved the following inscription, *Nectar of the Gods. And verily I say unto thee, thou must handle with great care for this shall be the holy vessel for God's own ale.*

Verily, this sanctified vessel is brought forth from within the vast wilderness of the holy goblet sanctuary with the least amount of delay. Additionally, these faithful gentles generously bring forth small amounts of any nectar newly released since my previous visit.

Today is another day of worship for those of us who are among the fortunate congregation of The Church of the Holy Nectar. A Celebration is in order, for surely the Church enhances our quality of life while bringing us inspiration and comfort.

Going to Beer Camp:
The Brewing of Love Potion No. 69!

*Sierra Nevada Beer Camp! Where big boys and girls can
experience life in a safe and nurturing environment
without their kids or spouses!*

WELCOME TO BEER CAMP! By way of introduction, I recently
completed a rigorous three-day Beer Camp-style marathon sponsored by Sierra Nevada Brewing Company of Chico, California.
Luckily my personal physician says that I should be able to enjoy a
full recovery within four to six weeks. Sierra Nevada's Beer Camp
is not for sissies. My first night at home after completing beer
camp, I fell into a state of suspended animation for over twelve
hours. When I finally surfaced the following day, the first thing that
came to mind was an old Bob Dylan line, *Well I wake up in the
morning, there are hops inside my socks ...* or words to that effect.
Beer Camp will do that to you.

The Camp experience is most accurately described as a one-
year course in craft brewing on an industrial scale condensed into
a seventy-two-hour period. It is a think tank for beer thoughts. If
there was a marketing brochure, it might read, *Welcome to an intense
three-day brewing session based on a military boot camp format.*

Many shall apply, few will be chosen: Just getting in was the
first challenge. Receiving an invitation to Sierra Nevada's Famous
Beer Camp is much like winning the luxury beer vacation lottery!
This rare opportunity is similar to the honor of being given an
appointment to Annapolis or West Point, or being awarded a
four-year scholarship to Stanford University. Biblically speaking,
It is easier for a camel to pass through the eye of a needle than it is for your

Budweiser or Miller drinker to get into Sierra Nevada's Most Desired Beer Camp. Do I hear an Amen? I was invited because I have spent in the general neighborhood of several hundreds of thousands of American dollars in Sierra Nevada's Pub, also known as *The Church of the Holy Nectar,* over the past fifteen years. That and the fact that I offered to write this story if I survived the Beer Camp experience.

I quickly discovered that those attending Beer Camp need to be in top physical and mental condition. I was once an honored guest of the United States Marine Corps back during the time of the Vietnam War. The Marine Corps graciously provided me with a grueling fourteen weeks of boot camp at Parris Island, South Carolina. Participating in Sierra Nevada's Beer Camp is in some ways similar to that Marine Corps Boot Camp experience, except with more beer and fewer sand fleas.

Don't fall behind! We began at exactly 8:00 A.M. of each morning. Stragglers who checked in late were told that the Camp train had already left the station, and if they weren't able to quickly catch up somewhere on the vast forty-acre brewery campus, they would be left behind to be eaten by the hop field wolves. For ecumenical comparison purposes, the entire Vatican City in Rome, at one hundred acres, is little more than twice the size of the Sierra Nevada Brewery campus.

The Beer Camp Counselors: There was a *tough love* attitude on the part of our two Beer Camp Counselors, Brother Steve Grossman and Brother Terence Sullivan. Our brains and bodies were constantly in motion and on the move. Campers who couldn't maintain the demanding boot camp pace but successfully evaded the wolves were *recycled* to test the new ten-ton composter unit recently installed in the *employee re-orientation* barn. This machine is able to blend all organic materials into a rich compost to be used in the adjacent hop fields and restaurant produce garden. It is widely known that Sierra Nevada Brewing Company is uber environmentally sensitive and produces all of their own compost. We were often reminded by our Counselors that lagging Beer Campers make rich compost.

The Beer Campers: The Campers were a diverse group of hopheads and publicans. One of the most interesting aspects of this Camp (which I am pleased to announce, fortuitously happened to be Beer Camp #69!) was the wide variety of colorful characters who had been chosen to participate in this much sought-after experience.

There were Campers from every region of the country. Among these worthies were two entrepreneurs from Boston who co-owned a trio of very successful upscale restaurants. These two characters were Jim Cochener and Mike, aka *Drew,* aka *Miguel* Moxley (every day his nametag inexplicitly listed a new alias. Someone in our group mentioned the tragedy of schizophrenia …). Then there was Pat Herbert, a gentleman beer distributor from Seattle, and Robert Parekh, a Manager of the Monte Carlo Casino in Las Vegas. The marketing line for this large-scale casino pub is *The Monte Carlo Casino, where you eat like a king and drink like the village idiot.* Also among these worthy Campers were two Irishmen, brothers Colin and Darren Comer. Originally from Dublin, these Irishmen own the Marlay House, a classic Irish pub in Decatur, Georgia, which was last seen being located in the immediate outskirts of the city of Atlanta. Their marketing program includes the phrase, *A Bit of Dublin in Decatur.* They have such a heavy Irish brogue that it is obvious they are not from around here, or anywhere nearby.

Two Campers hailed from Columbus, Ohio. Scott Schweitzer, who could double for Vince Vaughn (although Scott is the funnier of the two), is owner of the well-known Park Street Tavern, *A neighborhood tavern with over 240 premium beers on tap.* His tavern features–get this–karaoke night *with a band,* if you can imagine that! Talk about wretched excess. Also from Columbus was Jim Beatty, representing the historic Bob's Bar. By studying the Bob's Bar website, I learned that this business describes Columbus, Ohio as *The Cultural Hub of the Midwest*. I believe I can safely state that this is a little known fact to the rest of America. I always thought Cleveland was the center of Midwestern culture ….

The great state of Idaho was well represented by Brad Selvig, a partner of *The End Zone Bar* in Boise. This landmark pub, which is modestly self-described as *A Premier College Dive Bar* gives its location as being *Just a hail Mary pass from Bronco Stadium*. There is something about a *dive bar* being described as *premium* that seems counterintuitive. However, Brad says it works in Boise. Lastly, there was young John Flannigan, an owner of Flanny's Bar and Grill in Tempe, Arizona, which is another well-known college town. John was one of the more boisterous campers in the group and had to be placed in restraints several times during Camp Vespers. All in all, ten campers from seven states. A geographically diverse group of wild and wooly beer aficionados.

And then there was myself, not needing to be placed in restraints but slightly boisterous nonetheless. I am, and always have been, a certified Sierra Nevada pub *regular* (refer to previous story entitled *Worshipping at The Church of the Holy Nectar* for further details on that quasi-religious craft brewing sect). I was invited to take part in Beer Camp #69 after I offered to write an *outrageous made-up* story about it if I wasn't allowed to participate and get the real facts.

To round off the Beer Camper guys was a martini drinking executive-type gentleman from San Diego whom we think was headed north to Redding where he was to be the keynote speaker at an annual chiropractor's seminar. He apparently took a wrong turn somewhere off of Highway 99, and seeing the usual large group of cars congregated at the Sierra Nevada Brewery, mistook that for his conference location. He turned in and parked and, as they say, the rest is history.

Although Dr. Martini (we never learned his real name) had never visited a brewery before, he fit right in and was converted into a dedicated beer drinker before the end of the second day of camp. He didn't seem especially concerned that he was missing the opening session of the Chiropractor's Convention. He promised he would be back for the next Sierra Nevada *conference*. We learned several new French words as he was a French person, and every time he tried a new Sierra Nevada Ale, he would either say "Mon Dieu" or "Bon Dieu!" and once even "Sacre Bleu!" We think he liked the ales because he would then smile broadly and roll his eyes deliciously. N'est pas?

And then there was Ms. Beer Camper. The lovely Barbara Geshekter was the lone Camper of the female persuasion. Although she might be diminutive in size, Barbara is a very serious force on the current international microbrew blending and tasting scene. Some of her better-known blends include the much-respected Ruthless Torpedo and the recently formulated Little Big Foot Hoptimum, which compares favorably with Russian River Brewing Company's Pliney the Elder. Barbara is a reformed wine drinker, but she occasionally slips back to having her wanton way with the grape.

Barbara was invited to participate in Beer Camp and remember anything that I might forget, which was a lot. I blame it on the fog of brewing. I suspect Barbara also has more lively brain cells. However, she kept getting lost away from the rest of our little flock of Campers and was eventually awarded a small plastic compass found in a box of stale old Cracker Jacks so that she might keep up and not become dislocated. She will never earn the Trailblazing Merit Badge. Luckily she did not get misplaced anywhere near the composting barn. Again, as Camp Counselor Terence Sullivan wisely says, "Lost Campers make excellent compost."

The lovely Ms. Geshekter was always impeccably groomed. Once during an early morning lecture she excused herself to visit the lady's in order to touch up and generally fool around with her personal appearance package. When she came back into the lecture room with renewed lip-gloss and fresh face paint, all of us stood up simultaneously as we had been very patiently waiting for her to return so we could leave for a tour of the most important part of the brewery. That is the part where they served beer, through some high-tech device referred to as a *pigtail*, in tiny plastic cups very similar to what your personal doctor uses when he wants you to provide a lab specimen. Her comment when she entered the room and saw all of us stand up as a group was "Oy Vey! Such a bunch of little gentlemen. I walk into the room and they all stand up together. Such Mensches!" Then she handed out dainty little ribbon-tied packets of shortbread cookies to all the thirsty Guy Campers. Oy!

And it was at this point when it came to pass that the first mention of possible beer consumption was made for the day. Someone had to do it. This was at 8:28 on the first morning of Beer Camp #69. I noted the time on the back of a beer coaster. The specific suggestion was made by Scott Schweitzer of the well-known Park Street Karaoke Tavern, when he very much in character asked, "Hey, hold the croissants, where can a guy get some breakfast beer around here?" And thus Sierra Nevada's famous Beer Camp had officially begun. Sixty-eight beer camps had gone before us, but none could begin to equal the mythical Beer Camp #69!

Group dynamics in the *Fish Bowl:* Our first activity as a group was to report to the *Fish Bowl* conference room for an orientation session focused on the history of Sierra Nevada Brewing Co. This session was facilitated by Brother Steve. Our other Camp Counselor, Brother Terence was busy trying to track down a wayward Camper who was missing in action. A taxi was dispatched to the camp dormitory, also known as Oxford Suites, to search for him. Additionally an all points bulletin was issued with the local authorities. All local hospitals were checked, as were both local facilities of incarceration. Through various witness reports, it became known that the Campers assigned to the Oxford dorms had been out at a local pub the night before until last call was made as they carried out a rigorous quality-control campaign involving various Sierra Nevada products. The last sighting of the missing Camper was made as he performed a double backover flip off of his third floor balcony into the dorm pool. Brother Terence finally located the slumberhog still abed in the Oxford dormitory. He was brought to camp just in time to savor his first ale of the day, at 9:00 A.M. sharp.

Following the early morning orientation session, the Grand Wizard of the Sierra Nevada Pilot Brewery, one Scott Jennings, arrived to walk the Campers through an experiment in group dynamics, the like of which has never been experienced before. Within the span of one hour, twelve male Campers and one female Camper were to decide on not only what kind of beer we were going to brew over the next three days, but what it would look like, taste like, and be known as. This was a highly animated brainstorming session with a room full of Type A personalities.

Every Camper had his/her preferences and all were prepared to provide practical logic and personal emotions in defense of their pet idea. First we tackled the *type* of beer our product would be by going around the conference table with each Camper describing the type of beer he/she would like to brew. The desired beer types ranged far and wide. Three that come to mind were an ale with raisins and bran that could be used as a breakfast beer, a watermelon-flavored limp-wristed light-in-the-loafers lager and an India Pale Ale (IPA) with enough strength to stand up straight in the glass and salute the flag when served on the Fourth of July.

After a spirited demonstration of group dynamics, it was unanimously agreed that the official Camp #69 beer would be a strong amber ale of the India Pale Ale variety. In keeping with the spirit and essence of our session being Camp #69, the targeted alcohol by volume (ABV) would be 6.9 and the targeted International Bittering Units (IBU) would be 69. We would use many Bravo hops.

This was going to be a memorable beer–strong, patriotic, and hoppy. This description sounded very much like an old gal I used to go out with. Especially the hoppy part. Her name was Bunny, and I think she had some rabbit in her DNA!

The naming of Love Potion No. 69!
The next big issue was giving a name to our strong, tasty, and patriotic beer. Several less than objective suggestions were floated around the room, such as *Dublin in Decatur Double Bock, Park Street Tavern Live Karaoke Every Night IPA, Light in the Loafers Lager,* and *Old Slumberhog Hefeweizen,* as well as *Schizophrenia Stout,* in honor of Mike Moxley. Suddenly the brainstorming session came to an abrupt and unexpected conclusion with one excellent suggestion that brought forth unanimous agreement. One astute Camper, a local *pub regular* who shall modestly remain nameless, explained that there was only one natural name for the lovely new Camp #69 beer, and that was *Love Potion No. 69!* A rousing cheer of Huzzah! Huzzah! went up throughout the room as a group vote on the suggested name proved to be unanimous. Demonstrating their enthusiasm and support, several Campers voted twice while others carried the wise and handsome *pub regular* around the room on their shoulders. To celebrate the naming of *Love Potion No. 69,* the

pigtail was brought out and a round of spirits was served in those little plastic medical specimen cups.

Becoming beer scientists: After we completed our very successful work in the fishbowl, we were escorted on a tour of Sierra Nevada's numerous labs. First there was the quality control lab with its many extremely sophisticated scientists and much scientific equipment. One item of interest was described to us as *the coolest piece of science in the entire brewery!* That statement got our attention and as we were led into the laboratory's inner sanctum, we were introduced to a triple-x (XXX) sub-zero atomic freezer. This is where very exotic strains of yeasts were kept in a sub-atomic state of suspended animation until they were brought forth to be scientifically experimented upon. However, the coolest the freezer would go down to was somewhere in the neighborhood of 300 degrees below zero, which is cold enough to keep your ice cream nice even in the hot Chico summer, but not as cool as the temperature that an old girl I once went out with would get whenever I forgot her birthday.

Following this chilling experience, we were taken up to the Research and Development Lab where the famous Dr. Chris Baugh reigns supreme as one of Sierra Nevada's Senior Research Analysts. Dr. Chris is also known as *Doktor Strangelove.* This lab tour involved a marathon of major sensory information overload. First there was the Olfactory Sensory Lab, commonly referred to as *Chris' Stinky Shop.* In this scientific setting we were encouraged to smell samples of very old tennis shoes and gym socks, as well as a four-year-old mullet cake, under the guidance and close supervision of Dr. Chris, who proved to be capable of providing more scientific information than even the most astute Camper could possibly process. I recall asking at one point if I could be excused. "Please Dr. Chris, may I be excused. My brain is full." I was rewarded with a major stink-eye for that innocent question.

We were then handed off to the Tasting Lab next door where we were allowed to taste newly developed beers that none of the staff chemists wanted to risk trying. There were also some very elderly beers which the beer scientists wished to test on us to learn whether they were dangerous to consume or not. Beer Campers are expendable; PhD's in Chemistry, not so much.

Involved in this process was also the *blind tasting experiment.* In some breweries this involves a safe and sane side-by-side tasting experience where the taster doesn't know which beers are which, but none will usually result in vision impairment. However, this highly specialized quality control laboratory at Sierra Nevada Brewery, the finest brewery in all the land, had concerns about some new untested esters that were being used in an experimental new ale. We had heard through the hop vine (technically it is a hop *bine*) that overuse of these new compounds might, in rare cases, cause temporary blindness. We campers were brought into the lab to participate in a *Blind Tasting Experiment* to see if this might be true.

The famous beer bike: After our vision was fully restored and we were back on our feet, our next activity was a visit to the bottling plant at the other end of the forty-acre property. To get there as a group, we needed to use the notorious beer bike. Brother Steve has one of the best jobs during Beer Camp–piloting the beer bike back and forth and all about the large brewery campus (see photo). The beer bike is camper-powered. Each camper sits on one of the twelve sturdy bicycle seats and pedals away on regular bicycle pedals attached to a very complicated chain-drive system that turns an axle, which turns the tires in agreement with the pedaling of the camper. The overall appearance is very *Steampunk Meets Ringling Brothers Family Circus.* It looks like Leonardo da Vinci or maybe Jules Verne might have invented it back in the day. The beer bike is built on a BMW chassis and sports a gaily striped and fringed canvas top. Most important, it has a refrigerated beer keg built into the business end along with a generous supply of lightly salted nuts, as well as an unlimited number of those little plastic medical sample cups.

To us Campers it was like being the crew on a Viking slave ship. Commands were shouted into a bullhorn, and at the demand to "pedal!" we all strained our personal gizzards and began to slowly move the beer bike forward. As we gained a little speed, Brother

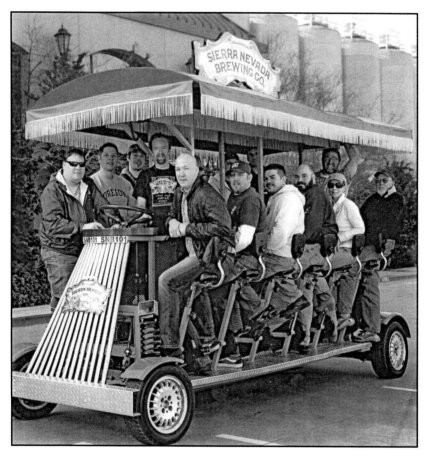

The famous camper-powered Beer Bike. A dozen hoppy campers halfway through the first day of Beer Camp. Scott Schweitzer wearing the shades on the far left just before he and his very large lunch rode the bike seat too hard. and broke it so completely off that it fell into the street! See Brother Terence Sullivan standing in the rear operating the keg of strong ale while Brother Jennings, the Wizard of the Pilot Brewery, pilots the steam punk Ringling Bros. Circus contraption. The lovely Ms. Barbara Geshekter and your author at extreme right. Fun was had by all. (photo by Bill Manley)

Steve would shout "Pedals Up!" whereupon we would pause significantly while he changed into a higher gear. After he engaged the new gear, he shouted, "Now pedal!" And so it went through all three forward gears. There was no reverse gear to concern us. Apparently we were in some sort of race because Brother Steve would often follow up his "now pedal!" command with "Harder! Pedal harder! Come on people, you can do better than that!" This command was often followed by the stinging crack of a whip and an admonishment that we all pedaled like a bunch of little girls, whereupon Camper Barbara would complain, "Well I *am* a little girl ..."

Visiting the bottling plant: We pedaled in this circus steampunk fashion all the way to the bottling plant. It must be noted here that the bottling plant is one of the most impressive operations at the Sierra Nevada Brewery. One million (that is 1,000,000) bottles per day pass down the line to be filled, capped, labeled, inspected and boxed all in one symphonic rolling operation. The two perfectly synchronized lines run nearly continuously while processing a total of 1,250 bottles per minute! The constant din of bottles rattling and stampers stamping and cappers capping is beyond belief. Everyone working in this huge plant must wear both safety glasses and earplugs at all times. It is rumored that some of the long-term workers have had their hearing temporarily removed so they didn't have to be bothered with wearing the earplugs all the time.

As Brother Steve allowed us to get off the beer bike and follow him through the main entrance, he checked every camper to make sure their earplugs were deeply imbedded into their earimentary canals, or somewhere like that. Just as the last camper, one of our Irish-American campers I believe, began to enter the building, and just as he inserted his earplugs, probably so far into his ear hole that he could practically taste them, the bottling line unexpectedly shut down! The plant was so completely silent you could hear a bottle cap drop at one hundred yards. However, our Irish-American brother wasn't aware that the bottling line had stopped as he was still around the corner and he famously commented, "Blimey! These bloody earplugs really work!"

Unfortunately, as we were returning to the brewery from the bottling plant, Big Scott, heavy with various ales and page three of the menu that he had enjoyed with lunch, sat on his beer bike seat too hard and broke it so completely off that it fell into the street! You can believe Brother Steve gave him a serious time-out for that!

The issue of merit badges: It seems like there should be some official award for attending Beer Camp as well as for crewing on the beer bike. I recall that once upon a time long, long ago when I was in the Boy Scouts, the earning and displaying of merit badges was very important to one's status within the group. The full uniform included a little badge sash that was worn across the chest, and there was nothing sadder than to see a sash, such as my own personal sash, with only one merit badge attached. I think it was an *attendance badge* for showing up at three meetings in a row. Hardly a heroic performance. I do recall my father, who greatly enjoyed his beers and ales, asking if there wasn't a merit badge given for brewing? I mumbled that I would check into the issue and get back to him. Little did I know that mere decades later, I would be deeply involved in an actual Beer Camp with the possibility of earning a merit badge in Brewing Arts or Beer Bike Crewing! An *Official Beer Camp Cycling Merit Badge* as well as a *Official Beer Camp Brewing Arts Merit Badge* were designed and awarded at the end of Camp. I earned both and now wear them proudly on my old sash, which I retrieved from my attic, right next to my Boy Scout *Official Three-Week Attendance Merit Badge.*

The legendary hospitality of Sierra Nevada Brewing Company: Overall, the hospitality of Sierra Nevada Brewing Company is legend. If campers can arrange to get to Chico, they can leave their wallets at home for the duration. Their money is no good while they are in Chico and Camper-guests of Sierra Nevada. Their every comfort is seen to by a very generous host brewery. Once the Campers arrive, they will find comfortable lodging conveniently located within easy walking distance of the brewery.

Much more important than mere human shelter, Campers are each issued a Beer Camp Pass that also handily doubles as a nametag. This pass allows the wearer to set himself, or herself, free in the pub where all nineteen beer taps are their personal playground. There will be no charge. However, all Beer Campers are charged with the responsibility of drinking with moderation. Throughout the three-day Beer Camp it became obvious that the new Ruthless Rye IPA was the hands-down favorite of the visiting Campers.

Furthermore, the Beer Camp pass allows each wearer to order off the exquisite Sierra Nevada Restaurant menu with great abandon. The story has been told that at one historic Beer Camp dinner, the enthusiastic and extravagantly bold brewers of Beer Camp #31 ran up a dinner tab of over one thousand American dollars. This was for a mere dozen hungry and thirsty campers! Camp #31 was comprised of all the *Pub Regulars* at that time.

The last time I checked, which was just yesterday, they are still the *Pub Regulars*. They lurk back by the pizza oven and are on site by 5:00 P.M. daily. As mentioned in another related story, if any of these *Regulars* fail to show up by five-thirty, which would be decidedly *irregular*, a welfare call is made to ensure that they are in good health.

During that infamous Beer Camp #31 the extremely flammable and highly explosive mixture these colorful characters brewed up was named Hoppy Camper Strong Ale. Not surprising, these dedicated *Pub Regulars* became known as The Hoppy Campers. Many of these brew outlaws are still working diligently to lose the extra ten pounds they gained during their Beer Camp experience. How did they gain all that weight in a mere three days, you ask?

Consider this: A $1,000 dinner tab for a dozen boisterous and hungry beer lovers averages out to approximately $85 worth of food and beer per Camper! And that was just one meal of many. Beer Camp is fully catered and is not for lightweights or those aspiring to be light of weight.

Fast rising new stars in the American Craft Brewing Industry. Sierra Nevada Brewing Company founders Paul Camusi, on the left and Ken Grossman, on the right, circa 1986. Grossman later bought Camusi out and became the sole owner. Photo is the front cover of the San Francisco Examiner, May 25, 1986.

Finally, with the official Beer Camp Pass, the Camper is allowed to shop in the Sierra Nevada Gift Store until they tire of selecting items from among the thousands of shirts, hats, beers, and other miscellaneous *brewania* items to be found there. *Brewania* is an official microbrewery term which loosely translates to *brewery souvenirs*. Needless to say, the brewania discount to Beer Campers is beyond generous. Lavish is the term. I wonder if my official Beer Camp No. 69 pass still works?

In concluding this highly scientific essay on craft brewing, all praise to Ken Grossman, Pope of the Church of the Holy Nectar, who has achieved the status of a deity within the international craft brewing industry. A toast as well to his worthy brewing family and to all the other gentles who brew the beer and make Sierra Nevada what it is today.

Furthermore, I would be remiss if I didn't offer up a special clink of the beer mug to Brother Terence Sullivan and Brother Steve Grossman, Counselors of the Camp, as well as to Father Al Spinelli, Minister of Good Will and Overseer General of the Church of the Holy Nectar. They have diligently kept us beer campers in close contact with our *Love Potion No. 69* brew as it ages to perfection in the holding tank. Brothers Sullivan and Grossman and Father Spinelli are all friendly and charismatic representatives of Sierra Nevada and much skilled in the use of the high-tech pigtail beer delivery system.

A little song to be sung around the campfire: This little song was written to be sung by young Beer Campers while seated around the campfire during evening vespers. It is best sung to the tune of the original *Camp Granada* by Allan Sherman.

Hello Mudda, Hello Fadda,
Here I am at Camp Sierra Nevada.
We got our earplugs and safety glasses,

We got our nametags and our bathroom passes.
All the Counselors love the waiters,
The mash tun is full of alligators.
We weighed our hop cones in a pail,
We cooked the wort, we dished, we named the ale.
Scotty went and broke the beer bike,
Now he's making compost with Boston Mike.
Mike's much smaller and less taller,
His new name is now Miguel Pub Crawler.
Please don't leave me in the hop field,
Or I might become a wolf meal!
Please Brother Stevie, don't make me stay,
I've been at Beer Camp already One Whole Day!

Update: It has now been six weeks since all the *Huzzahs* were shouted in the Fishbowl Conference Room at the conclusion of the planning and development of *Love Potion No. 69.*

It may interest the reader of this Official Beer Camp Follow-Up Report to know that just four days ago, during the time of the solar eclipse this most recent Thursday past, *Love Potion No. 69* was finally released in The Church of the Holy Nectar. The overwhelming demand for this exotic brew far exceeded the supply of ten kegs to be made available to the drinking public.

Let it be known that several Church records were broken when this excellent strong ale with subtle undertones of raspberry and chocolate was consumed down to the dregs of the last pint within slightly less than four Pub Days of business.

Some local Astronomers say the Great Annular Solar Eclipse of 2012 influenced this record-breaking rate of strong ale consumption! Here's to Astronomy!

PART FIVE

FAMILY STORIES:
YOU JUST CAN'T MAKE
THIS STUFF UP!

My Brother Had Issues with Fish

ONCE UPON A TIME many years ago, back during my formative period, roughly between the ages four and twelve, I lived among the fish eaters. This was on Pawleys Island, just off the coast of the great state of South Carolina, which is near the lovely historic oceanside community of Georgetown. During those years I was forced to eat fish every day of the week except Friday. We ate meat on Friday. We were Protestants.

Of some possible interest to students of geography is the fact that Pawleys Island was then only loosely attached to the rest of the state by a rickety old wooden bridge. Pawleys Island would occasionally become detached from the mainland as a result of the numerous force-five hurricanes that my brother, Dixon Roy Kilbourne, A Great American and Christian Gentleman, and I grew up eagerly looking forward to. I was an only child except for the one brother, who had embarrassing issues with fish.

Back East, as well as in the Arctic Circle, schoolchildren wait for *snow days*, or *glacier days* in the case of schoolchildren living in Antarctica, which give them a reason to miss school in the middle of the week. On the coast of South Carolina, in that region referred to as *the low country*, we eagerly awaited *hurricane days* to give us that same welcome break from school. We would rather be swept out to sea, or blown all the way into Georgetown, than go to another day of school.

As was mentioned, during all those years that my family and I lived on Pawleys Island among the fish eaters, our primary diet staple was food provided by the ocean, which my Sainted Mother called the *ocean's bounty*. My family spent years surviving on local fish and the occasional starfish stew, which my inventive mother made into a primordial recipe that also included sea anemones, periwinkles, and fiddler crabs. The periwinkles gave the stew a crunchy texture, which nicely contrasted with the salty sliminess of the sea anemones.

I recall the one basic building block of most of our meals was the mullet, which was not a type of awful hairstyle back in those days. These mullets were an awful-tasting, very bony fish. Your ocean-dwelling mullet is widely acknowledged to be the bottom of the natural order of the *ocean's bounty*. It had a taste that was so strong, and so overwhelmingly fishy, that even our old hound dog, Mr. Chumley, wouldn't go near one, dead or alive. In fact, if we wanted to keep old Chumley off the furniture, all we had to do was rub an elderly mullet on the upholstery, and that usually took care of our problem with Chumley, as well as with persistent unwanted visitors.

Your fully-grown mullet smells so fishy that even when it is ground up to be used as fertilizer, and lavishly treated with Old Spice aftershave lotion, it still cannot be used in the garden until after all the neighborhood cats are safely locked up. This precaution is to prevent them from becoming overheated and frantic in the special way that southern cats will do. Manufacturers sometimes substituted the younger mullets as flavoring for cat toys when catnip wasn't available. Using the Old Spice didn't improve the flavor at all.

While desiring to not offend the United Mullet Workers of America (UMW of A), the only other legitimate use for the mullet that I know of is as projectiles at the Annual Interstate Mullet Toss sponsored by the infamous Flora-Bama Lounge and Package Store in Perdido Key, Florida.

During those idyllic days growing up on Pawleys Island, my father was the Manager of the Chamber of Commerce in nearby Georgetown. Although he dearly loved his work, I believe his total salary, including tips and free grits credits, was around $5,000 a year.

This was all the money there was in our budget to provide for myself, my brother, and my Sainted Mother's every need. My father didn't personally need very much, just a few bottles of Schlitz beer, *The Beer That Made Milwaukee Famous,* and the occasional bushel of raw oysters, which he slurped down one by one with great gusto, first adding a liberal dash of Tabasco sauce to each. My mother claimed that my father wasn't fully civilized. She said he could be a vexation at times.

Living on this limited annual income, we didn't have a lot of extra money with which to buy extravagant items such as milk, peanut butter and jelly, and bread and butter and other regular food items considered part of the *grocer's bounty.* Of historic note, we had two grocery stores in the low country back in those days. Lachicotte's was the larger and possibly more modern one. The other, smaller grocery was owned by Mr. Frank Marlow, a friend to all, and a true Southern Gentleman.

Therefore, although my brother and I craved Moon Pies and Nehi Orange Crush from Mr. Frank's, we most often lived on fish as a source of low-cost protein. After all, your mullet could be purchased all day long for a mere five cents the pound. Unfortunately, about four pounds of your average five-pound mullet was a collection of fish bones of every possible description. Some of the bones didn't even look like they should be found inside a fish. I recall one strangely shaped bone that was simply referred to as *the elbow.* Now I have given this elbow issue some considerable thought over the years, and I cannot for the life of me imagine where a fish's elbow might be located. If there was a fishbone referred to as *the knee,* that would make much more sense. Everyone knows that fish have knees, which come in handy whenever they have to kneel down.

However, while the mullet smelled and tasted horrific, I will concede that from a point of freshness, nothing beats buying your dinner while it is still flopping around on the slickery deck of the fishing boat. My mother, my brother, and I would go shopping down to the fish docks around mid-afternoon, while the crews were returning from being out upon the sea since before dawn, after working hard at fishing and drinking beer all day.

My brother was *special,* and was once officially diagnosed by the College of Charleston Mental Health Department as having *issues with uncooked fish.* This was long before sushi became a highly popular item in upscale restaurants. So whenever he was allowed to accompany my mother and myself on our weekly shopping trips down to the fish docks, he had to be restrained with a stout chain harness that we had purchased at Marlow's.

My brother had an awkward habit of yelping and flailing around on the deck of the mullet boat as it was still docking, while viciously attacking the still flopping fishes with his sharp little milk teeth. He loved his fresh mullet. This behavior was always led to an embarrassing moment for my Sainted Mother and myself. More than once the SPCA, which also served as the Mullet Rescue Organization, had to be summoned.

Most times my father would not be able to accompany us on these exciting weekly fishing expeditions down to the docks as he would be busy out on the golf course developing *important plans* for the upcoming *Miss Shrimp and Grits Festival and Parade,* or some similar event that the Chamber of Commerce organized and sponsored. He sternly insisted that his job was very important and was not to be taken lightly. A lot of his work seemed to involve playing golf with his Chamber Board of Directors and other downtown business leaders.

My mother claimed that mullets were *economical.* For the cost of one American dollar, a person could buy enough of your mullet to feed a family of three for nearly a week, whether or not you relished them as my brother did. My father didn't require much solid food, other than his bushel of oysters every few days. I urged him to stop with the oysters already, as this constant diet of shellfish was causing him to pay worrisome attention to my Sainted Mother, and I didn't want any more siblings. The weekly embarrassment I already had to endure with my brother's antics down at the docks as he scampered after the fresh mullet was plenty enough.

The result of my being forced to eat so many low-life, bottom-feeding fish back in my formative days growing up on Pawleys Island, near the lovely and historic seaside community of Georgetown, is that now, as an adult, I have sworn off seafood for life. I have no intention of ever going back to that awful habit. In fact, for many years now, I have belonged to a twelve-step program for former fish eaters. It is my intention to never get outside of another fish. Nowadays, thinking of mullet gives me the howling skitters.

Growing Up as a Free-Range Child

MY ELDER BROTHER, DIXON ROY KILBOURNE, a Great American and Christian Gentleman, and I grew up as free-range children. During our formative years, while being raised up in the lovely community of Aiken, in the great state of South Carolina, we were not hindered by parental rules and regulations of any sort. About the only thing we were told, and disciplined about if we failed to listen, was that we must be polite to our elders and respectful of all women at all times. Other than that, we were on our own. *We weren't feral, but we were definitely free-range.*

While I was growing up in this free-range sort of way, my parents both worked, although only one of them ever got anything useful accomplished. My father, Harry Kenneth Kilbourne, was Manager of the Chamber of Commerce while my Sainted Mother, Gladys Mae Kilbourne, was his Executive Secretary. This was a two-person operation located within a tiny historic log cabin on Richmond Avenue. My mother accomplished most of the day-to-day managerial activities as my father spent a lot of his time out on the Palmetto Golf Course during regular work hours. He played golf with his buddies on the Chamber Board of Directors so he felt his time golfing was *work-related.* His casual work schedule went well beyond the traditional *half-day Wednesdays.* In my hometown, for some curious reason, when the week got around to Wednesday, all commerce stopped promptly at 1:00, right after lunch. Even the barbers closed up shop. This was an accepted and unquestioned tradition in a small southern town where eccentrics and golfers were in charge.

Our free-range upbringing was especially apparent when my brother and I were kicked out of the house early on Saturday mornings, right after a big breakfast of bacon and grits with ham and red-eye gravy. We were told not to come back until dark. *We had to forage for lunch.* In the summer we went swimming down at the Eustice Park Pool, where you could swim all day for the price of one quarter. We practiced our dives in order to impress and disrupt the girls, especially the lovely Sharon Murrill-Surasky and her sidekick, the equally lovely Margie Lou Gaver. The splash-worthy *watermelon* dive was the most popular, and most disruptive. The girls would spend hours fussing with their hair and makeup while gossiping endlessly about who did what to whom at school. We figured those girls needed a good splashing.

In the colder months, when the pool was closed down, I would get up on Saturday morning and, following the usual hearty breakfast of bacon, I would walk to town, which was a three-mile downhill hike as we lived in *Aiken Heights.* My weekly allowance of two American dollars would be burning a hole in my pocket. The chores by which I earned my allowance included doing the dinner dishes within one hour after the meal was finished, and washing the family car on the weekend. My father liked his cars, and I recall that one favorite of his, a 1950 Cadillac DeVille, was a cream and green *two-tone* fastback sedan with whitewall tires and fender skirts.

On those Saturday mornings I took myself to the picture show at the Patricia Theatre on Laurens Street in beautiful downtown Aiken. The morning showing of that week's Saturday feature cost twenty-five cents. Usually the movie was an Abbott and Costello comedy or a western featuring cowboy heroes such as Roy Rogers, Gene Autry, or the Lone Ranger. Sometimes it was a Dean Martin and Jerry Lewis comedy, or one of the Bob Hope and Bing Crosby series, such as *On the Road to Bali,* or somewhere else far removed from my little hometown of Aiken, South Carolina. Aiken was the county seat, with a population of approximately 6,000, plus or minus a few hundred.

During the movie I would enjoy a popcorn and coke, which cost the princely sum of twenty cents total. I was now down to $1.55, part of which was carefully saved for the grand piece de resistance, a hot fudge sundae with whipped cream, nuts and a cherry on top, which would set me back another twenty cents. Over the years of my childhood, this fabulous treat was served to me hundreds of times at Blake's Pharmacy on the corner of Laurens Street and Richland Avenue. I was a creature of habit, and I knew what I liked. Blake's Pharmacy had an authentic soda fountain with a long marble top and the old-fashioned vinyl-covered, round-topped stools that spun so you could see all the girls when they came in to replenish their makeup supplies for the coming school week.

I personally did not need to see any girls coming into Blake's Pharmacy because the lovely Marlene Updagrove was already there, working behind the soda fountain each and every Saturday. And believe me, she had my full attention. She was *well developed* in a way that caused her little rayon soda fountain uniform to stretch and strain at the fragile little buttons whenever she inhaled, which was usually several times a minute. I paid much more attention to the workings of Marlene's respiratory system than I did my own.

After this weekly delight, and when I could not bear to admire Marlene any longer, I turned to the magazine rack where I could choose from one of the following magazines: *True, Argosy,* or *Stag.* These *outdoor adventure* magazines had much in common as they all seemed to feature adventure stories involving bears. Grizzly bears to be specific. Great big grizzlies that stood over eight feet tall when they reared up on their hind legs. Most of the stories began something like *I was attacked by an eight-foot-tall grizzly bear that was reared up on its hind legs, but my dog, Mr. Fluffy, saved me from sure death.* The story then ended with something like, *Has anyone seen Mr. Fluffy? If so, please contact ....* Occasionally, if I couldn't find a magazine that appealed to me, I would go to the paperback bookrack that rotated and twirled for the shopper's convenience.

There might be a hundred or so random titles in the rack that were refreshed every few weeks. The cost of these *pocket books* was one quarter. I recall one of my favorite books from Blake's Pharmacy was Maritta Wolff's *Whistle Stop*, which was *steamy* and would have certainly been rated strictly PG-18 if it came under today's censorship laws. I believe I still have that book around here somewhere, well hidden from my fourteen-year-old daughter, Savannah A. Kilbourne, the finest daughter in all the land, whom I guarantee will not be reading it anytime soon. Right after I had finished the book, my father read it and enjoyed it greatly. He wanted to know if I had anything else by Wolff that he might also enjoy. My father was very open-minded and did not concern himself with matters such as censorship. He felt the issue of what books should be available to children was strictly a matter of personal choice. A free-range sort of philosophy. I recall that I was twelve at the time.

Another popular item to be purchased at Blake's Pharmacy was a Marchand Hair Treatment Kit with which you could *peroxide* your naturally brown hair into a toxic nuclear yellowish-green color. All it took was a package of Marchand and some strong sunlight to cook it. To accomplish this awful magic, you went home with the package and mixed the several deadly ingredients together in the little plastic tray that was thoughtfully provided along with the little plastic mixing paddle. The plastic tray began to steam and bubble soon after the several ingredients were combined. You had to act quickly before the mixture melted through the tray and onto your lap.

You then found a comfortable place on the back steps in the direct sun, got out your reading material of choice, and then combed the lethal combination of chemicals into your hair. You waited exactly one hour. No more and no less. After this amount of time had passed, you went into the bathroom and admired your new peroxided blonde hair. At this point, you always had a moment of hair dyer's remorse. This ugly effect would last until either your hair grew out, or fell out, whichever occurred first.

I remember once, in the wintertime when there wasn't enough sun to effectively peroxide my hair; I dyed it from brown to bright green by using food coloring, which was available at the nearby Piggly Wiggly *chain store*. (Surprisingly the Piggly Wiggly didn't actually sell chains, but the Hoggly Woggly Grocery down the street did.)

Our parents were different from some of the more traditional and conservative parents of our peer group. Our parents took a strong liberal stance on racism and women's rights. The *N-word* was never spoken in our home, and in fact, I don't believe I ever heard my father curse in any way. Not even a mild hell or damn, except the historic time when he scored a hole-in-one on a beautiful Sunday morning, while the rest of us were worshipping inside of St. Thaddeus Episcopal Church, where my Sainted Mother later served as Church Secretary for many years. I recall that Father Hickey was the Pastor at the time. When my father came home that special afternoon, after the *Heavenly Hole-in-One*, he exclaimed that he had made a "hell of a fine shot on the sixteenth hole, which had a moderate dogleg to the left." That was a strong statement for him.

Another sport my father greatly enjoyed was the game of pool. At one time he was some sort of pool champion and actually made enough money to buy his first car that he named Popocatepetl, which is an irritable volcano in Mexico, because the car was always boiling over. He taught my brother and me the basics of pool and would take us down to City Billiards, located on Richland Avenue in lovely downtown Aiken. He would give us outrageous handicaps and if we managed to beat him, which was seldom, he would buy us several chilidogs. Those pool hall chilidogs were at the top of my feeding chain during my formative years although I didn't get to eat very many free ones. If our father beat us, which was most of the time, we were allowed to pay for his beer for that particular game. He rarely paid for his beers when we were playing against him. Luckily the chilidogs were only twenty cents so we could afford to pay for those as well as for the beer.

Our parents were a pair of cerebral beings, and I often wondered if they might be aliens from the planet Zoldar, which had been prominently featured in that week's Saturday matinee at the Patricia Theatre. At one time, they were the state champions in Contract Bridge for couples; and during another period, my father was the state chess champion for several years, and actually played one game with a Russian chess master that took nearly a year to complete. This was before the invention of the Internet so they sent their moves back and forth via the U.S. Postal service on penny postcards. The parents of some of my friends thought that the game of chess was just *fancy checkers* and that bridge was what connected the opposite sides of a river.

Cerebral as he might be, my father was not fully connected with the concept of being a parent. He simply referred to my brother and myself as *the boys*, as in, "Gladys, I haven't seen *the boys* in a few days now. Are they still living here?" At the time I was twelve and not likely to have moved out on my own, although the thought had certainly occurred to me from time to time. I suspect he would be hard pressed to answer correctly any specific question having to do with my age, grade, or middle name. I was just the smaller of *the boys*, of indeterminate age or placement in school.

The safety of the general public seemed to be a very casual thing when I was growing up. Beginning driving age in South Carolina was fourteen-and-a-half, when one could acquire a *probationary* license, which required that you have anyone over 18 with you when you drove. It could even be a blind person or your great-grandmother. However, at the age of fifteen, you could have your full license and you were on your own, flying down the highway in the family car, all by yourself. You were probably sitting on a cushion so you could see over the steering wheel, and you were going fast because you were in a great hurry to go nowhere in particular. The issue of personal safety, and how it directly related to driving carefully and well, did not enter the new driver's consciousness.

Even more unbelievable from a public safety point of view is the following fact, that should be published in a *Ripley's Believe It Or Not* column. I was a full-fledged school bus driver at sixteen years of age! This was just after finishing my sophomore year of high school. The only requirement was a regular driver's license and a clean record, and some brief and casual school bus driving training during the summer before you were to become an official school bus driver and employee of the State of South Carolina. This intensive instruction amounted to a total of about ten hours of training, five in class and five behind the wheel, which, in my case, including driving the school bus down to the A&W Root Beer Stand for lunch. I took over my brother's bus route and his cadre of screeching little girl admirers after he went off to be abused at the Marine Corps Boot Camp at Parris Island, South Carolina, where I would blindly follow him two years later. But that's another story.

Over the years I also inherited several other of my brother's cast-off and worn-out jobs. When I was twelve, I took over his *Aiken Standard and Review* route. The weekly subscription rate was twenty-five cents, which I collected on my route monthly. That would amount to an entire American dollar being owed each month, and some subscribers asked that I collect weekly so that it "didn't add up so much."

Back in the day, there was a burning desire for all the guys at Aiken High School to *be cool*. We guys were overwhelmed with hormonal secretions way beyond our control or understanding, and as a result, did and said things that were completely ridiculous in order to *be cool*. For example, when observing an attractive *chick* out on the dance floor at Scott's Lake, moving to the beat of the music, it was cool for a guy to shout, "Shake it but don't break it. Wrap it up and I'll take it." How cheesy is that?

Back in those days, buying beer and wine was allowed at eighteen years of age in South Carolina, but you had to be twenty-one to buy whiskey. We shopped for our alcohol at an earlier age than was allowed by the state by going down to Mr. Tebow's Grocery at Six Points, where it was known that you could buy beer if you were tall enough to reach up and place your money on the counter without being boosted up by someone else. Long arms helped.

Beer was $1.25 the six-pack, and you needed a *church key* opener to get the beer out of the can. This was years before the invention of tab-top cans, *a modern miracle*, or twist-off bottle caps. The beers of choice back in those days were Budweiser *(The King of Beers)*, Schlitz *(The Beer That Made Milwaukee Famous)*, Pabst Blue Ribbon *(America's Favorite Beer)*, or Carling's Black Label *(Twenty-Four Headaches to the Case)*. I believe the very first beer I ever drank, at the tender age of fourteen, must have been a Carling's Black Label because I distinctly recall having a headache the following day.

Another, more effective means of quickly becoming intoxicated to the point where you might be comfortable shouting "Shake it but don't break it. Wrap it up and I'll take it" out at Scott's Lake, was through the ingestion of just a smallish amount of *white lightning*. This powerful liquor, very similar to liquid LSD, could only be bought by driving the big yellow school bus out into the country, over several one-lane dirt roads, until you arrived at a tarpaper shack with a corrugated tin roof. There was no age requirement at these distinguished places of business.

You never shopped for white lightning alone. You always brought several buddies along for moral support. After you arrived, a flurry of coin tossing would determine who had to get out and approach the shack in the dark. The terrified customer knocked on the rough pine door and then, as a dim bulb came on over your head, and a peek-a-boo window slid open in the door, you had to say, "Pinky sent me." You then showed a dollar bill, held up in plain view. You smiled disarmingly if you could. At this point a disembodied hand with a pint fruit jar of clear elixir came through the small window. You placed the dollar in the hand before the jar was released. You did not touch the hand. If you wanted more than one pint, the process was repeated, including knocking on the door again. However, you only needed more than one pint if you were responsible for providing all of the liquid refreshments at a large party involving several dozen participants.

In order to be swallowed with the least amount of pain, the elixir was mixed half and half with R C Cola or some other strongly flavored beverage, such as grape Nehi, in an attempt to mask the taste. However, this effort was doomed to failure as the musky, bitter, greasy flavor of the white lightning refused to be overcome.

We soon learned to enforce a firm No Smoking rule once the jar had been opened. I vividly recall the time a jar of white lightning exploded in smoke and flames after the fumes had been exposed to a spark. The resulting damages to the family sedan were difficult to explain.

In this historic photograph, taken at the beautiful Brookgreen Gardens, in the heart of the South Carolina Low Country, my grandmother, the storied Hazel Barnes Kilbourne, discusses when and where the next delivery of "Hershey's Products" will be made. Photo circa 1950.

Hazel Barnes Kilbourne,
A Stout Woman of Largish Appetites

MY GRANDMOTHER, HAZEL BARNES KILBOURNE, was an unforgettable character. She was a stout woman of European descent with largish appetites. Most often the target of her appetite was chocolate. Anything chocolate would do, but most especially *Hershey's products* rang her chimes nicely. She was strictly forbidden from eating sweets because of her condition, which she explained by saying that she suffered from *the diabeets*. She would go on further to say that she was also *eaten up with the arthritis*. One health-related fact after the other. What she failed to mention was that she was also overweight by one hundred pounds or so, give or take a stone. A lot of this excess had to do with the abuse of chocolate.

She habitually wore a giant corset about the thickness of a one-inch sheet of steel-reinforced marine plywood as well as what appeared to be a four-pound bulletproof brassiere. Entire whales gave their lives up to donate enough whalebone to provide the necessary structural strength to make these *foundation garments* contain herself all in one general area.

Her diabetes condition was supposed to keep her far away from chocolate as it was a poison to her system, but this medically proven fact did not discourage her in any way. She was always on the hunt for chocolate, much like a bluetick hound is always on the hunt for the fat opossum. However, instead of baying like a hound on a hot scent, her dentures set up a violent clacking whenever she came within snapping distance of any form of chocolate.

Hazel Barnes Kilbourne, a largish woman, was also a very sneaky grandmother, and she often involved myself as an unwilling accomplice. My participation was required to help satisfy her forbidden lusting for chocolate. While she was supposed to be taking care of my elder brother and me, it turned out to be the other way around. She waited until I got home from school at three o'clock, after a hard day of studying and memorizing all the important details of the wily coeds, and then her demands would begin. A typical scenario would go thusly. "Davie! Davie! You Davie! Come here right now. I need you to run me a favor." The insistent voice was coming from the rear of the house, where my grandmother lived. She referred to it as *her domain*. Her parakeet *Birdie* kept her company. A *Birdie* would die from time to time, and a new *Birdie* would appear within a few days. The parakeets changed but the name always stayed the same.

I knew what she wanted when she called me back into her room. She wanted me to go to Mr. Tebow's Grocery, which was down the road and over the bridge, and buy her a new supply of secret hide-away chocolate. "You Davie, take this dollar right here that I am holding out to you, as I want you to go right down to Mr. Tebow's and get me some Hershey's products. Now we both know that the chocolate bars cost five cents each so I want you to bring me back twenty of the bars with your almonds in them. When you get back, and after I have counted them all up, I will give you one for yourself to eat. You won't need to mention this trip to anyone else in the family because it will be our secret, as usual. Now get going because I have a powerful craving for one of those bars."

"Why don't you ask Dickie to go?" I would plead. "I'm right in the middle of my quadratic equations homework and he isn't busy. All he does is play with his dolls and toy soldiers." She would grimly respond, "Now you know good and well why I am not able to ask your brother to run me a favor. He has loose lips! The last time I asked him to go pick me up some supplies, he let it slip to your mother that I was back on the candy again. Loose lips sink ships! Plus he doesn't like chocolate the way that you and I do, and he wanted me to give him a quarter to go to the store! That's highway robbery! Here I am, his grandmother and *eaten up with the arthritis* and all. For shame!"

When I got back from the store, and after she had carefully counted all twenty of the Hershey's products, she would hand one over to me and say, "Go ahead, you can eat it right now if you want." I would protest that I probably shouldn't eat it just before supper. She would retort, "Well, who's watching? You need to get rid of the evidence before your mother gets home." My mother, the Sainted Gladys Mae Kilbourne, was the bane of my grandmother's existence as she had appointed herself to serve as the *sugar police* and was always checking for telltale signs that my grandmother had *been at the candy again.* There were numerous empty Hershey's products wrappers to uncover as well as the secret hoard of chocolate that was always kept hidden deep in my grandmother's closet.

Other abuses of her grandsons included her insistence that we play cards with her instead of wastefully spending our afternoons doing homework. As soon as we came through the door, overwhelmed after a long day of school studying the wily and elusive coed, Hazel Barnes Kilbourne would begin with, "Boys, we have to play a few games of Canasta to keep our minds sharp." She loved playing cards, and Canasta was her favorite game. She was a riverboat gambler at heart and often wore a green eyeshade. Unfortunately, she had to depend on my brother and myself to play as all of her friends had been burned in previous games of chance with her. She liked to play for pennies. She would say that it was "just for fun," but by the end of a long afternoon of struggling over a double deck of losing Canasta cards, we both would have *donated* our allowance for the coming week.

Winning our meager allowances at Canasta was just one of the ways that my grandmother took care of us after school while my parents were at work. They were blissfully unaware of the crimes that were being visited upon their innocent children by the wayward Hazel Barnes Kilbourne. As we played through the afternoon, we kept an eye on the clock and made sure to end the game before they got home from work. Well, my mother actually got home from work. My father usually got home from golf.

In addition to beating us at Canasta like redheaded stepchildren, my grandmother greatly enjoyed reading her *main magazine,* as she called it, which was a monthly publication entitled *True Romance.* This steamy publication strictly focused on illicit love affairs, breakups and makeups, and all the exciting activities in between. She craved this magazine almost as much as Hershey's products and had her calendar marked so that she would have the magazine in hand on the same day that it hit the magazine rack at Mr. Tebow's Grocery. Sometimes the magazine was so fresh that the ink was still damp.

Besides the *True Romance* magazine, there were other publications she also read religiously, but they were not of the same caliber when it came to getting her misty-eyed and breathing at an accelerated pace. She also had *her shows* on the little television set in her room and never missed *Days of Our Lives* or *As the World Turns.* To round out her constant diet of stories of illicit romance and related misadventures was a collection of paperback books that littered the surface of her bedside table. These little paperbacks could best be described as *bodice rippers.* The richly illustrated covers never failed to catch and hold the attention of my runaway hormones. The colorful designs always featured some voluptuous damsel in distress with her flimsy bodice torn and shredded and her amazing cleavage exposed. She would be in the arms of a swarthy and mustachioed swashbuckler or pirate or other virile hero as she was being saved from sure death, or at least from being severely plundered. I recall the book *Mandingo* was always prominently displayed on her little bedside table, ready for reading at a moment's notice.

My wayward grandmother also had several other vices, including having several snifters of her medicinal *schnapps* every night before dinner and the unfortunate fact that she was a vicious smoker. It was a disgusting sight to watch my grandmother smoke a cigarette. She smoked Pall Malls long before filter tips were invented, and she would wrap her lips around the business end of the cigarette and literally soak and make sodden a full inch of it while she balanced another full inch of ash on the other end. She could never find her ashtrays even though we had placed nearly a dozen of them around in her room.

In all fairness, it should be noted that all this cigarette abuse occurred back in the day when doctors were featured in tobacco company ads proclaiming that smoking was good for you and was, in fact, an excellent stress reducer. The ads actually showed doctors, complete with stethoscopes hanging around their necks, smoking a cigarette with a satisfied, stress-free smile.

The very worst thing my grandmother ever did to my brother and me was to declare Sunday evenings as her time of the week to cook dinner. She said that she enjoyed spoiling us with some good old-fashioned home cooking since my mother worked all day and was only able to prepare quick, very tasty and popular dishes, such as spaghetti and meatballs. It was with a great flourish that my grand-mother would take over the kitchen at mid-afternoon on a Sunday and prepare "some real food, like a nice boiled tongue" for us, even though she always said that we were in grave danger of being spoiled with this delicacy. Ruined and sickened was more like it. The tongue had the general appearance of fresh road kill and tasted as we imag-ined the reproductive organ of a buffalo might taste.

Along with the evil-smelling boiled cow's tongue, she would proudly prepare something called corn meal mush, as well as gen-erous portions of Sauerkraut for each of us. "Don't worry, there's more where this came from," she would assure us as she served up generous portions. In preparation for this weekly gourmet feast of boiled tongue and equally challenging side dishes, my brother and I always snuck a loaf of bread and jars of peanut butter and jelly out of the kitchen and into our room around mid-afternoon on Sunday. In this way we could say in honesty that we weren't hungry when the boiled tongue was passed around.

After dinner, my grandmother was a very *regular* sort of person. She used the bathroom once per day and that seemed to satisfy her needs. Our home was a one-bathroom home, built before the invention of multi-bathroom homes, and she chose to be regular as clockwork, which was about one hour after evening vespers. From long exposure to this olfactory trauma, my brother and I always tried to get our bathroom visits accomplished before her evening effort. This was because the bathroom could not be used, or even entered, or even walked by, for at least one hour after she had completed her transaction. This air pollution was especially horrific on Sunday evenings. She would breezily say that it must have been the tongue.

She was, however, kind enough to mention when she *felt a stirring in her nethers* so if anyone wanted to visit the bathroom before she did, "now is the time, or forever hold your water." She then asked if anyone wanted to get into a friendly little game of Canasta when she came out. She would say, "Only for a mere penny a point, just for fun."

One of the biggest thrills in my grandmother's colorful life was to *go for a motor on the pike.* She didn't care what the destination was, or who was driving. If she wasn't asked to go along, she would pout outrageously for days. If the car was going to the grocery store, not Mr. Tebow's Grocery, but to a big chain grocery such as the Piggly Wiggly, she would sit in the car while we were inside and gossip with anyone coming within the range of her considerable voice. She was a master of random conversation and could always find some connection with any unfortunate who happened to walk by.

Not surprisingly, my grandmother, Hazel Barnes Kilbourne, a stout woman of largish appetites, always insisted in stopping at the Dairy Queen for an extra large chocolate frosty cone on the way home. She promised to *treat* if we would stop. When we objected based on her health risk, she swore that chocolate ice cream was exempt from the diabeets restrictions. She had read that fact in her *True Romance* magazine.

My brother, Dixon Roy Kilbourne, a Great American and Christian Gentleman, and the author, yours truly, who is holding Barker the Pig, also known as Little Mr. Pulled Pork Sandwich, in a loving embrace while surreptitiously giving his perky little hams a good feeling up. Note protective mesomorphic posturing of elder brother toward author as he gently hums a few bars of He Ain't Heavy, He's My Brother. Photo circa 1950.

He Ain't Heavy, He's My Brother

WHEN THE MEMORABLE EVENT upon which this story is based occurred, I was a mere slip of a lad of ten-going-on-eleven while my brother, Dixon Roy Kilbourne, a husky brute of a boy and general all-around good brother, was twelve-going-on-sixteen. He was a strapping physical specimen and *big for his age* according to our neighbor next door, a lusty widow lady who kept a close eye on his development. It was obvious that his growth glands were on a whole different schedule from mine.

My brother had a classic *mesomorphic* body type, which is scientifically described as *naturally stronger and heavier, possibly shorter and stockier … and clueless about the opposite sex.* My body type, on the other hand, is *ectomorphic,* which is scientifically described as *slender, sensitive, possibly smarter and more heroic, and typically more admired and desired by the opposite sex.* Scientifically speaking, body typing is a good thing if you are an ectomorph. Not so good otherwise.

We were always *Dickie and Davie* to all our friends and family. As in, "Dickie, stop all that writing on your Sunday School sermon for a few minutes and come in here where you can help us disentangle Davie apart from this nice neighbor girl so he can get your homework finished." Dickie was big for his age in physical development while I was more *advanced* in the fine arts of love and romance. It was said that I was purely *a natural* when it came to being a favorite of *the ladies.* My father was very proud of my God-given talents and would often brag to his golf buddies about my amazing exploits at such a young age. He said that I was precocious in certain ways. I was a healthy young ectomorph.

On the other hand, Dickie was interested in only the most wholesome things. Much like his hero, Karl Kleencut, the protagonist of George Vermont's excellent little tale *Adventures in Oatmeal,* Dickie always jumped out of bed at sunrise on Saturdays and did a quick fifty pushups before brushing his teeth vigorously, being sure to massage his gums. He then dressed in tighty whiteys, heavy denim jeans, and a clean white T-shirt. His footwear consisted of a pair of stout cushion-sole hiking boots, with built-in arch supports, which he had chosen for their smart good looks and durability.

After completing his early morning routine, he would briskly stride into the kitchen where our sainted mother would be waiting with a twelve-cup stewpot brimming with steaming oatmeal. This would be topped with a full cup of wheat germ, ground spinach and barley sprouts that Dickie insisted on having with all his meals. He washed down the pot of oatmeal with two quarts of fresh whole milk and would declare himself ready for a day of hiking in the crisp winter air. He would then sprint next door to the home of the Everclean brothers where he would roust them out of bed with his cheerful greeting, "Hello boys! Are you ready to start on that twenty-mile jog to Brookgreen Gardens while singing robust German hiking songs?"

On the other hand, I would still be deep under the covers, having been up very late the night before escorting the entire Georgetown High School Cheerleading squad down to the abandoned cabin by the lake, where we had cocktails and canapés while engaging in healthy boy-girl activities.

While Dickie was so serious and mature it was sickening, I did have to teach him pretty much everything he ever knew about girls. He just couldn't get the handle on boy-girl situations. While he was stockier of the two Kilbourne boys, I was the more quick-witted. Also, even though I was a full two years behind him in school, I had to help him with his homework more times than was good for the proper development of his mesomorphic brain cells.

Furthermore, in addition to patiently training Dickie about boy-girl matters, I had to save him from danger so many times that it was almost a rerun of *Lassie,* a popular television show in those days. Lassie was always coming to the rescue of Timmy when he fell down the well. I clearly recall my own experience when Dickie fell down the well, twice, and I had to run and tell Grandma. Dickie would always holler up to me in his trusting voice, echoing up from the bottom of the well, "Davie, you have to run and tell Grandma that I've fallen down the well, again." I raced as fast as my little feet would carry me. When I got back to the house I was panting heavily from the hard run, my tongue hanging out and my little brown eyes crossed. I wasn't able to talk, but Grandma was there to figure out what I was trying to convey. "Why, I think he's trying to tell us that Dickie has fallen down the well, again. Look, I think he wants us to follow him."

Another time Dickie was trapped in a burning barn, and again I had to run and tell Grandma that he was in peril. Then there was the time he fell through the crust of a burning sawdust pile, and another time when the roof of an abandoned mine shaft caved in on him. Probably the most heroic event was the time I saved him from the clutches of Marlene Updagrove, a mature young woman whom the gods of physical largesse had broadly smiled upon. She was *blessed* in that certain highly developed way. She lived on the other side of the railroad tracks from us and used to come calling late at night, around nineish, which, while I was just getting ready to go out for the night, was well after Dickie's healthful and sensible bedtime of 8:00.

She was quite a bit older, probably thirteen, and had a craving for either my clueless brother or some other hapless mesomorph. I did the heroic thing and saved him from embarrassment by telling her that he was strictly dedicated to maintaining the purity of his bodily fluids and not interested in fooling around with any girls. I further mentioned that it was a church thing. However, I went on to say, I would help her out in her time of need if I could. It was only a short time later that we were going steady and I was, once again, involved with an older woman.

Our father, Harry Kenneth Kilbourne, known to one and all as *Ken,* was the *Executive Director* of the Georgetown Chamber of Commerce. He qualified as a *community leader* since he wore a suit and tie to work every day. He truly loved his job and spent more time there than he did at home. I think golfing and deep-sea fishing with his friends had something to do with his chronic absences from home. Sometimes he would combine these two hobbies by driving old golf balls off the back of the boat while waiting for a big tarpon to attach itself to his line.

The rest of the family liked to think of ourselves as *farmers* since we lived away from the downtown Georgetown area in the small community of Friendfield Farms, where we had moved after we left my early childhood home on Pawleys Island. As a young farmer, I raised pet chickens. They were pets because we never ate them. Another thing that qualified them as pets was that each and every one of them had an individual, personal chicken name. The hens of the flock all had names beginning with the letter *H,* such as Henrietta, Helen, Hazel, and Harriet, while the two roosters each had a name beginning with the letter *R,* as in Roscoe and Randy Rooster.

As a young farmer boy, I also had a pet pig named *Barker.* He earned his name because of the noise he insisted in making whenever he needed to be fed or required special attention. Barker, whom I fondly referred to as *Little Mr. Pulled Pork Sandwich,* almost ate us out of house and home. He grew from a five-pound piglet into a ninety-pound shoat in less than six months. His appetite was legendary, and he would eat chicken eggs faster than we could gather them.

At this time I admit freely and without shame that I had designs on his personal pork, and I think he finally became aware of that sad fact. He may have gotten that idea because he was a smart pig, and I was always calling him over and giving him a good feeling-up every few days. I lovingly massaged his shoulders and hams to make them tender. *Tender loving care* is what he got from me. I was (and still am) a big fan of pulled pork, and perhaps my copious salivation in front of him was a dead giveaway. The fact that I used to affectionately rub a sweet mustard-based sauce on his shoulders and perky little hams may have been another hint of what was to come. I recall Farmer Brown visiting from next door one day and wondering out loud how a pig could get around on just three legs. I said, as if anyone should be able to understand this obvious phenomenon, "A pig that good, you don't just eat all at once."

Every Sunday Dickie and I would trudge down the road to attend services at the Friendfield Farms Presbyterian Church, where he was the *Sunday School Assistant.* My complete humiliation associated with this was almost beyond my ability to bear. What kept me going Sunday after Sunday was the quarter that my mother gave each of us for the collection plate. However, I was usually making my contribution at Mr. Tebow's grocery, which was directly across the street from the church, well before Sunday school began.

At Mr. Tebow's, you could get a cardboard cup of ice cream with a tiny wooden paddle-shaped utensil for ten cents. The good thing about the little ice cream cup was that on the underside of the cardboard lid would be a photo of your favorite movie stars, which you would collect and then trade with your friends. My favorite pictures were those of Hedy Lamar and Yvonne DeCarlo, which were worth three pictures of Randolph Scott any day of the week. You had to carefully lick the lid clean of ice cream if you wanted the best picture. However, you didn't want to lick it too briskly or you would lick the picture right off the cardboard.

After that you could get a R C Cola and a small bag of Planters peanuts to pour down the neck of the bottle for another ten cents. This left me with a nickel, which almost looked like a quarter if I covered it with my hand when I dropped it in the collection plate. Dickie didn't notice most of the time, even though he had been warned to keep a vigilant eye on me throughout the church service. Most of this unwanted attention from him resulted from my known habit of *worshipping* with Marlene Updagrove back in the vespers room.

However, I have gotten off the track regarding what this story is actually about. Once upon a time it came to pass that I had invited the entire Georgetown High School Girls' Swim Team to meet me down at the old swimming hole on the other side of the railroad track on a Sunday after church. I had some new strokes that I wanted to show them, and I thought it would be better if we were alone, all together.

I clearly recall that memorable Sunday when I was down there doing my heroic Tarzan vine swing out over the pond, showing off in my ectomorphic sort of way. While doing a particularly dramatic swing, I somehow became disengaged from the vine and plunged headfirst into the deep end of the pond. It should be known that those special ones of us blessed with ectomorphic body types sink like stones without adequate floatation devices. We should not be allowed near any body of water larger than a standard eight-ounce drinking glass unless closely supervised. All the girls got into a competitive struggle, pushing and shoving at each other in an attempt to be the first to rescue me. I was in danger of being drowned by all these high-spirited young girlies! Just at that moment, as I was going down for the third time, I saw a host of heavenly angels wearing gentle smiles, beckoning me to come unto them. I felt pretty sure they were the same ones my father heard when he scored his heavenly hole-in-one. Just as I was following the angels into the radiant light, lo and behold, my big brother Dickie, a husky brute of a boy with mesomorphic tendencies, appeared out of nowhere. He jumped in, grasped me chokingly about the neck and began shouting, "I got him! I got him! Stand back, all you young girls, and give little Davie room to breathe!"

Unfortunately, as I stood up, I stepped directly on the broken neck of the Pabst Blue Ribbon beer bottle that I had cast down several weeks earlier when I was at the old swimming hole with the entire High School Girl's Track Team. I had been showing them some of my new dance moves. All of us alone, together. Well, the blood fairly gushed out of my main foot artery and, if truth be told, the sight of it began to make me feel a little dizzy in the head.

At that point, my brother, Dixon Roy Kilbourne, a great American and local hero, saved me instead of the usual other way around, when he was always at the bottom of the well, again. He hoisted me upon his naturally stronger and heavier mesomorphic-type shoulders and commenced to carry me the entire one mile back home while singing loudly, and repeatedly, in his husky brute of a voice, *He Ain't Heavy, He's My Brother* by The Hollies. He was really getting into the lyrics. *The road is long, with many a winding turn ... but I am strong enough to carry him ... cause he ain't heavy, he's my brother.* He was just getting to the part that goes, *his welfare is my concern, no burden is he ...* when I blew chunks of my boiled peanuts and grits breakfast down his sturdy mesomorphic back.

After a long hike uphill with the hot sun beating down upon us, we finally got home. He never put me down, even once, although he was huffing and puffing like an enthusiastic jenny mare in season. When we came in through the front door, our grandma, who was a freak for any and all card games, shouted, "Oh my God, you've finally gone and killed that poor little devil! Don't let him bleed out on the carpet. Does anyone want to play a nice game of Canasta?"

Although this heroic ending to a potentially very tragic scenario happened many years ago, the memory is still kept just as fresh now as then. Possibly the reason the memory is still kept so unfortunately fresh is that every time I see Dickie, which has been a few thousand times since that memorable day, he holds forth at great length about how he saved my life that afternoon down at the old swimming hole while the entire girls' swim team looked upon him with raw animal lust. He then unfailingly breaks into *He Ain't Heavy, He's My Brother,* until someone mercifully switches him off.

Growing Up as the Son of a Soothsayer

MY FATHER, HARRY KENNETH KILBOURNE, was a self-certified soothsayer and *pyramidologist*. He professed to be a *visionary*, whatever that was. That's right, during my formative, and most emotionally vulnerable years, I was *raised up* as they say in the South, as the son of a soothsayer. While residing under the same roof, and watching the same *I Love Lucy* shows, I lived with someone who firmly believed the pyramids were constructed by beneficent aliens from outer space.

As a means of verifying this amazing statement, the following is a direct quote printed in the August 5, 1975 *Aiken Standard and Review*, a daily newspaper of good reputation and excellent circulation. I have the original news article at home if anyone wishes to review and confirm this. As follows:

> *Ken Kilbourne, the Aiken County (S.C.) Psychic Group Founder and Chairman, is convinced, following extensive research, that the Great Pyramid of Cheops was not built by Egyptians but by a superior cosmic civilization. Kilbourne sides with the theory that the Great Pyramid was constructed in cooperation with ancient astronauts, or possibly by the people of the lost island of Atlantis. Kilbourne goes on to further elucidate that the ancient Egyptians simply didn't have the technology to design and construct these monuments, although they may have invented the refreshing beverage commonly referred to today as beer.*

This last beer-related fact won the ancient Egyptians everlasting appreciation and respect from my father and his chronic golfing buddies down at the Chamber of Commerce. On Sundays he entertained no thoughts of visiting St. Thaddeus Episcopal Church, where the rest of the family would be, as he felt golf was all the *spiritual* experience he required. One summer Sunday he had what he referred to as a *Heavenly Hole in One* at the exact same time the rest of us were languishing inside the hot and stuffy church. I'm sure I was wearing my little clip-on church tie at the time. This lucky shot caused him to immediately withdraw to the clubhouse bar, where he was pleased to buy his chronic golfing buddies a round of good Egyptian beer while entertaining them with statements of how he had experienced a vision of that ball dropping on a score of one well before he teed off. He was a visionary in that regard.

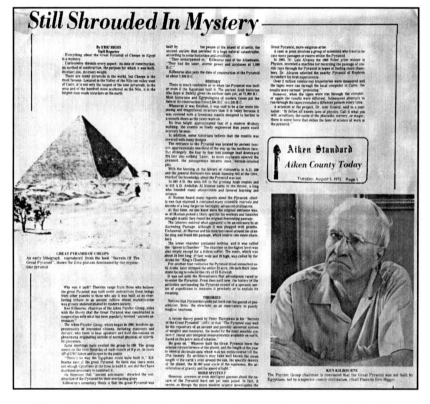

Therefore, let it be said up front and out in the open: my father was not always *in the moment,* as they say these days. His mind was tuned to a station the rest of us couldn't hear. In addition to his psychic interests, he also avidly believed in reincarnation and read all of the books by, or about, one Edgar Cayce of Virginia Beach, N.C. These books often discussed the virtues and benefits of age regression as a means of determining who, or what, we had been in earlier lives.

My Sainted Mother also believed in a modified version of reincarnation and always wanted to come back as a seagull. I believe I had a conversation with her feathered self during my last visit to Pawleys Island. Since she passed away several years ago, I talk to seagulls whenever I have the opportunity.

My father's group of psychic cronies often met at our house for an afternoon of testing various occult theories they had either studied or come up with on their own. I dreaded coming home from a long day at Aiken High to find a miscellaneous collection of cars, winged chariots, and sometimes a broom or two, parked in the driveway.

I had been burned before on my father's various arcane experiments in levitation as well as other activities, especially the one that involved hypnosis and then dancing the hula with a lawn flamingo. This fact may go far in explaining why I still get a startled *deer in the headlights* look whenever anyone asks what my childhood was like. The one *psychic experiment* that I remember most clearly was a testing of the concept of levitation, which involved the ability to cause objects to become suspended in thin air through the application of highly focused psychic energies.

I clearly recall that particular day. I was an innocent child of thirteen years and had been suffering from impure thoughts since the start of my second period Biology class in which the lovely Marlene Updagrove was my lab partner. We were currently studying reproduction. She was wearing my favorite sweater, and she knew it. But I digress.

It was a Thursday that particular day, and I had seen the winged chariots and brooms parked in the driveway and knew there might be trouble. I secretly came in through the back door, which was also the nearest entrance to the refrigerator, which was an important appliance to my growing self. I was in the middle of my every-day after-school ritual of creating a triple-decker peanut butter, bacon, grits, and jam sandwich to be washed down with a large glass of chocolated buttermilk when I overheard my father say, "Let's try Davie. He's long and skinny, and I think we can float him."

After overhearing my father's comment, I immediately went into stealth mode while trying to disappear from the kitchen into my bedroom where I could eat my after-school creation in peace and harmony. Unfortunately, the living room was in the way of my escape and I didn't get very far before my father suggested that I come over and join them *just for a minute or two.* I was justifiably filled with trepidation, as I had been the victim of my father's *psychic experiments* before. But, always the obedient child, I cautiously entered the room to find my father and a group of his psychic cronies arranging three straight-backed chairs in a row. I felt strongly that nothing good was going to come of this. My concerns were not addressed.

It was explained that I would put my heels on one, my backside on the middle one, and just the back of my head on the last chair. After I was fully settled and relaxed, several special psychic phrases would be spoken, a quantity of Egyptian Beer would be tested for aging and general quality control, and then the middle chair—the one that was supporting 95 percent of my total 120 pounds of grits and butterbeans—would be slowly and gently pulled out from beneath me. If things went as hoped, I would remain suspended with my only support coming from just the tip of my head and tips of my heels. Several couch pillows were placed under me just in case the psychic forces and atmospheres weren't in alignment that day.

It did seem like I remained suspended for a magical moment, until my floating sensation was rudely interrupted by the undeniable call of gravity.

The Heavenly Hole In One

Ⓘ IT WAS VERY DIFFICULT TO GET MY FATHER, Harry Kenneth
Kilbourne, to attend church inside of an actual church building.
It's not that he was an atheist or agnostic or claustrophobic, it's
just that, as he patiently explained every Sunday morning, he
chose to worship in a different way, to do his churching out on
God's own green golf course. My father entertained no thoughts
of sitting indoors on a beautiful Sunday morning. He felt his golf
game was exactly as much *spiritual guidance* as he required on a
regular weekly schedule.

My mother, Gladys Mae Kilbourne, a truly sainted individual
if there ever was one, badgered him on the church issue for many
years before eventually giving up on that fruitless endeavor. I believe
she finally reconciled herself to his chronic absence from church
by admitting that he was just not *fully civilized.* She felt there were
many worse ways he could get into mischief than playing eighteen
holes and having a couple of beers with his golf cronies from the
Chamber of Commerce. After all, fresh air and exercise couldn't be all
bad, and he was especially good at getting into some sort of mischief
or other if he wasn't kept busy. I recall one of his more noteworthy
mischiefs involved his narrowly winning a regional pocket billiards
tournament where he had exceeded his cash-on-hand budget and
was forced to wager the pink slip for the family sedan. Even when
he proclaimed that the car was never in any *real* danger, and pool
was *just a game,* my mother was not amused.

I was an only child except for my brother, Dixon Roy Kilbourne,
a Great American and Christian Gentleman, who was a church-going
sort of boy in no need of my mother's persuasion. I believe there might
have been a mix-up at birth because, at seventeen years of age, he was

the youngest Sunday school teacher in the history of our church, the Church of the Carolina Low Country, in lovely Georgetown, South Carolina. When my heathen friends at school learned of this horrific fact, I had to bring forth some creative mischief in order to offset the social stigma.

Unfortunately, after finally giving up on my only partially civilized father, my Sainted Mother focused her considerable powers of church-going persuasion on myself. I was known as the *more difficult* of the two Kilbourne boys and was often *a challenge* for my mother when Sunday morning rolled around. This was especially true if I observed my father preparing for a day of sunshine and fresh air while I was fussing with my little clip-on church tie.

Worshipping out on the golf course during a long Sunday morning of devotion to shooting below par was not a casual thing for my father. He always took great care with his provisions as he packed several cans of beer, some ice, two cans of boiled peanuts, and then a couple more beers, into the bulging pockets of his old golf bag. If he needed more storage room for beer, sometimes he would leave out a golf club or two.

My father worshipped diligently in this way for so many years of Sundays that he should have been appointed an honorary Bishop or Monsignor, or something. *Brother Kilbourne and the Heavenly Church of the Holy Sand Trap and Water Hazard* sounds about right.

Once upon a time, after all those many Sunday mornings of faithful worship on God's own golf course, *Brother Kilbourne* miraculously scored a hole in one. The historic occasion took place on the sixteenth hole of the Georgetown Municipal Golf Course, which was a par 3, 180-yard stretch with a modest dogleg to the left. This hallowed event occurred during the exact same time that the rest of us were languishing in a hot and stuffy church, where I was wearing my bankrupt penny loafers and my little clip-on church tie. Well, my possible brother, Dixon Roy Kilbourne, *Youth*

Pastor in Training, wasn't languishing as he was busily preparing his Sunday school lesson plan.

Later that evening, long after church was over and it was full-on dark outside, just before vespers, as we were warming up the television set for the *Ed Sullivan Variety Hour,* my father returned home amid a great clanking of empty beer cans, boiled peanut containers, and golf clubs. He seemed to glow with a reverent demeanor and beatific radiance, brought on, at least partially, by the large number of Schlitz beers *(The Beer That Made Milwaukee Famous)* that he was forced to imbibe in order to lighten his overloaded golf bag. Dropping his depleted golf bag and three remaining golf clubs on the front porch, he proudly exclaimed that he had scored a hole in one!

He went on to explain that just as this once-in-a-lifetime sanctified event took place, the following occurred, in his own words: "I knew that I had hit a good clean shot. It cleared the Devil's Frog Pond by only a yard or so and then came back into view as it rolled up on the green and then,"*and here he paused dramatically,* "the instant the ball dropped into the cup, I saw a bright light in the sky parting the very heavens, as if through a stained-glass church window, and then I harkened to a heavenly chorus, the like of which I have never harkened to before, and the spirit came over me."

He was breathing heavily and rolled his eyes upward mightily at this point while saying he was convinced it was the Mormon Tabernacle Choir in high gear with a seasonal fireworks display. We had accidentally seen them on the television once, without any fireworks, while we were waiting for the *I Love Lucy* program to begin.

Being his loquacious self, and possessor of an inner child that was happy and ready to play at all times, my father went on to enthusiastically explain that immediately following this hallowed epiphany, on the hazardous par 3 sixteenth hole, the rest of the game was promptly abandoned. He was then quickly escorted by his golfing buddies from the Georgetown County Chamber of

Commerce to the nearby clubhouse that was appropriately named the *19th Hole*. One of his golfing buddies was the infamous Smiling Jack, the Stunt Pilot. My Sainted Mother claimed Smiling Jack didn't have *good mental hygiene,* a condition that accounted for a wide variety of personal quirks and habitual misbehaviors. Back when I was growing up on Pawleys Island, in lovely Georgetown County, there were people living inside the state prison who were accused of having done nothing more than have poor mental hygiene.

Still standing in the doorway, because he was avidly smoking one of his big Cuban cigars and wasn't allowed inside the house with it, my father went on to explain that it was there, at the refreshing *19th Hole,* where he was allowed to buy a succession of sacramental rounds of Carling's Black Label Beer, with their well-known marketing slogan, *Twenty Four Headaches to the Case,* for those thirsty golfers who had borne witness to the holy event. This traditional ceremony of buying high-quality beers for the witnesses was a longstanding policy and a form of Holy Communion on those extremely rare Sundays when some lucky Christian scored a Heavenly Hole In One.

PART SIX

UNFORGETTABLE
CHARACTERS
I'VE KNOWN

The lovely and adventurous Nancy Lynne (Kanga) Quiggle, in full Girl Scout counselor uniform, while planning the dinner menu for twelve little Girl Scout Cookies. *She is considering inflicting her Grandmother's Authentic Pasta Sauce upon them. The little cookies must have behaved very badly that day to deserve such harsh punishment. Photo circa 1964.*

Nancy Lynne Quiggle, Girl Scout Counselor in Charge and Backwoods Chef

ONE OF THE MOST INTERESTING PEOPLE I'VE EVER MET, under the most unusually pleasant circumstances, was my former, first, ex, and only wife. Her name was Nancy Lynne Quiggle, and at the time of our first meeting, she officially introduced herself to me as *Kanga, Girl Scout Counselor in Charge.* She had just recently turned eighteen years old, but you wouldn't have guessed it. She had a good running head start on life and had already been dismissed with cause from two universities, a fact that didn't seem to compromise her amazing sense of self-confidence in any way.

I originally crossed paths, actually the trails to Juniper Lake and Horseshoe Lake, with Nancy, aka Kanga (all the girls had taken names from *Wind in the Willows*) while hiking up in the backwoods of Lassen Volcanic Park, in Tehama County of Northern California. I recall our initial meeting that morning up on Flatiron Ridge as it was that memorable time when my crew of seasonal forest rangers and I were invited to experience her Grandmother's Polish/Armenian *Old Country Traditional Spaghetti Sauce.* At the time, Nancy-Kanga was camping, and counseling, with a medium-sized covey of little Junior Girl Scouts, sub-species category Brownies or Cookies or some similar bakery designation.

She had that sort of *European* look of a uber healthy nature girl model-type, and I clearly recall immediately trying out my infamous #7 pick-up line on her, which goes something like this: "Nancy-Kanga! You smell good! You smell like you have been taking a bath in rainbows and cupcakes!" This corny line had never worked before, and in fact, wasn't even appropriate, as she actually smelled like an interesting combination of pine trees and bacon. However, it must have stirred up some need to feed in her because, after a lot of outrageous eye-rolling between herself and her co-counselor, also newly eighteen but not nearly as advanced, she promised us a *fine homemade dinner of spaghetti and all the trimmings* if we would visit their campsite later that evening and deliver a case of cold beer and four gallons of hearty red wine. Oh, and a quart of chocolate milk for the little Brownie Cookies. The request seemed reasonable at the time.

Nancy Lynne Quiggle, Girl Scout Counselor in Charge, carefully explained that this alcohol was part of the list of necessary ingredients for the traditional old country authentic spaghetti sauce recipe for the dinner to which we were invited that evening. She made it clear this list of *necessary ingredients* was for herself and her co-counselor only. If we required anything for ourselves, we were to bring that also.

We arrived on time with all the alcohol we could gather up because (1) there were two attractive young Girl Scout Counselors, who smelled deliciously like bacon, available to receive our pent-up attentions, and (2) the fine Italian-Bavarian, or whatever, home-cooked dinner would be the first real civilized food we had been offered in nearly a month. We had been subsisting mainly on old and slow chipmunks and random quail eggs.

Upon arriving at their campsite later that evening, and as a largish pot of unfiltered lake water was placed over the meager Girl Scout campfire, we settled in and began passing around a gallon jug of thick red wine while the organic lake water for the pasta heated deliciously over the fire. These two young counselors were very much thirsty and in the mood for a hearty drink of classic Santa Paula fine wine before dinner. The jug was gurgling near empty before the unfiltered lake water had reached a full boil.

This rate of consumption was somewhat of a concern to myself and my crew, as the wine had set us back $1.99 each gallon at the store over in Chester. We wanted to slow things down just a little. In any case, we knew we were in for a fine gourmet Hungarian-Lithuanian, or whatever, dinner, and we all began salivating heavily, in a healthy young forest ranger sort of way. We were somewhat bemused to not see any evidence of the many ingredients, other than the vast quantity of alcohol we had provided, that must be necessary to bring such a excellent meal to its final state of glory. However, we were all young guy college students on a summer forestry job and didn't pretend to understand the finer points of exotic cooking that women concern themselves with. We understood forest rangering. We did not understand cooking.

After the water was at a full boil and most of the microbes were either dead, or at least well-done, Nancy ceremoniously dumped in a 5-pound bag of spaghetti noodle shards, and what appeared to be several leftover biscuits from their Girl Scout breakfast, which she had been carrying around in her bottomless army surplus jacket pocket. This pocket also contained a well-worn book of poetry entitled, *The Complete Works of e. e. cummings and His Famous Broken Typewriter,* as well as a pack of cigarettes, which were kept in a metal band-aid box. The band-aids had apparently been discarded in favor of putting the box to a better and higher use that, it was explained, was to prevent the cigarettes from becoming *rump sprung,* which we learned, was an official Girl Scout term.

After this patient tutorial on how to protect cigarettes and other drugs from the elements, she delicately helped herself to yet another fruit jar of the fine hearty red wine. Soon after the demise of the second gallon, and immediately prior to the unscrewing of the third, the two Girl Scout Counselors, who seemed to be setting a very questionable example on Young Lady Decorum Merit Badge Studies for the dozen or so little bakery items they were supposedly mentoring, administered the final exotic ingredient to the six or seven pounds of smashed-up noodles and waterlogged biscuits swirling in the pot, by dumping a 64-ounce bottle of regular store-bought catsup, with the 49¢ price stamp still attached, into the pot and proudly announced, "Dinner is ready!" The old world Greek-Basque, or whatever, spaghetti sauce was actually made by a Jewish-German company named Heinz!

A hush fell all over the crew and myself as we sat in wonderment at the ease with which these two exotic young wood nymphs seemed to operate. It was almost like they had magically thrown the meal together right in front of us through the use of some female sleight of hand. We understood trees. We did not understand girls.

Now fast-forward to later on that evening, after the authentic, old world spaghetti and hearty red wine supply had been depleted and all the little brownie-cookies were tucked in and fast asleep in the cook shack.

For it was later that memorable evening, not long after vespers, when I was personally introduced to the *Girl Scout Counselor Way with Young Forest Rangers.* I recall being awarded several merit badges before the sun rose over Juniper Lake and the smoldering campfire that next morning.

A Short History of the Friday Evening Gentlemen's Billiards Society, LLC, Est. 1988

COME ONE, COME ALL, to the Friday Evening Gentlemen's Billiards Society, LLC. This loosely knit social organization, which has met regularly for over twenty years, or approx. 1040 times, convenes each Friday evening of the year at the DownLo Billiard Academy, from 5:00ish to 7:00ish, rain or shine. Ladies are encouraged and always welcome.

Membership in this unique cohort is composed of two levels with the first level being the *Regulars,* which are those having no friends, no family, and nothing better to do. These ne'er-do-wells maintain regular attendance unless they are either temporarily incarcerated or suffering from disabling emotional issues.

The *Regulars* include a varying number of local worthies as well as one judge who quietly offers favorable results in cases coming before him for the fee of one pint of Sierra Nevada's finest for misdemeanor charges or two pints for felony cases. His personal credo is *all the justice money can buy.*

Other regular players include several local attorneys not wishing to be named due to possible litigation issues, as well as a professor emeritus, a reconstituted monk, and a magistrate of unknown provenance. Then there's myself and a shady individual known only as *The Monsignor* who, it is reputed, has close ties with the Costa Nostra.

The second group, the *Irregulars,* is made up of local worthies having family, friends, and/or usually something better to do. These gentles drop by and make their financial contributions as time permits. These *contributions* are made on $1 per game basis with the game winner sometimes winning the princely amount of up to $4.

Occasionally a visiting pool hustler-type will see the dollars flying around and troll by the table with their professional sensors at high alert. However, after watching our game, in which we make up the rules as we go, and can involve as many as thirty balls and a small stuffed armadillo on the table at one time, they soon drift away shaking their heads in disbelief.

Spectators who have made a hobby of watching the zany antics of our group, the Friday Evening Gentlemen's Billiards Society, LLC, are fond of saying we have been trading the same couple of old worn-out dollars back and forth within the group for the past twenty years. The best among us, if there is such a person, might be as much as $12 or $14 dollars ahead after two decades of hard playing.

It becomes quickly obvious to any spectator that skilled pool shooting is not nearly as important as the more serious question of who is going to buy the next round. With that said, it should be mentioned that over all these years, the group has established a long-term loyalty to Sierra Nevada products. While this writing is certainly not a specific endorsement for that exquisite local product, if some random keg happened to be left off at the DownLo Billiard Academy (319 Main St.) for quality control purposes, it would be dealt with gently and respectfully.

From a historic perspective, the current DownLo Billiard Academy was previously Team Players, and the original owner, one Jeff Hilgert, was a pool shooter from the old school. He was always willing to give us lessons *for a few dollars per game* and was very hard to beat. We finally devised a handicapping system where he was forced to shoot one-handed while balancing on his left foot and singing old Frank Sinatra songs in a loud voice. In this way we were able to beat him maybe half the time.

The Friday Evening Gentlemen's Billiards Society, LLC first played at Chico Billiards and then at a pool dive called Piggy's after Chico Billiards closed. The action at Piggy's was random and hectic and often offended our finer sensibilities. More than once we arrived on a hot summer afternoon to find several of the Piggy's regulars playing in their underwear, only. They often *took it outside*, again in their underwear, to settle a disputed shot.

The Friday Evening Gentlemen's Billiards Society, LLC, Est. 1988. Shown are, (left to right) Michael, Geordie, The Judge, yours truly, Richard, and Braddon, who is enjoying an attack of flatulence.

Conditions have improved greatly since the days of Piggy's, and we now have a delightful new face with the recent arrival of the new DownLo House Pro, Jacqueline Karol, aka *The Angel of Billiards*, who is now organizing pool leagues as well as giving lessons. Contact Angelofbilliards.com

While Jackie presents herself as the image of youthful innocence, we quickly learned that she channels the Great White Shark when she has a pool cue in hand. It can be very dangerous swimming in her waters. There have been stouthearted lads who have gone into *friendly* games with her never to be heard from again. Lessons anyone?

The last known photograph of Humbert J. Uncle Humpy Wilkins. He is seen in this photo wearing his magical spectacles, which he said were "photoelectric" and would turn dark when in the direct sunlight, or sometimes even when not. Uncle Humpy had a luxurious growth of thick blonde hair and always wore his Little Lord Fauntleroy hat and frilled ascot as he felt it set a fashion trend while giving him a youthful demeanor.

    In the unlikely event that Uncle Humpy is seen anywhere, anytime, especially in British Columbia or Tasmania, the witness is asked to contact the local authorities at their convenience. Under no circumstance is the witness to contact the author of this book.

The Adventures of Uncle Humpy and Baby Jaws
Or
Nothing Less Than Excess
Is Good Enough for the Likes of Us

MY BOON COMPANION AND LONGTIME FRIEND, Humbert J. *Humpy* Wilkins, has never been someone to shy away from extreme over-indulgence and excessiveness of any sort, at any time. *Nothing less than excess is good enough for the likes of us* has always been his mantra. During his colorful lifetime, he has never met a drug, or any form of alcohol, he couldn't work with. His escapades are legend and his hold on reality has always been tenuous at best. He can go days without knowing where he is.

I have known this unforgettable character longer than almost anyone I am acquainted with who is not a member of my immediate family. I first met him in a scuffle on the playground of the William C. Bynum Elementary School, in beautiful Georgetown, South Carolina, where we contested over a very old and rusty folding pocket knife. I ended up with the prize and he held a grudge for several days. Later we got into another battle over a hot game of marbles, which I let him win in the spirit of fairness. Even in the face of that harsh beginning, I have still maintained a nearly life-long friendship with him.

I have to thank his sainted wife, Flynndra B. Wilkins, for she served as the catalyst and glue in our nearly lifetime-long friendship. She knowingly signed on as Humpy's lifelong caretaker when she married him back in their grad school days. Flynndra is a very well-grounded, nurturing person of Tunisian descent. For the past many years Flynndra has devoted a great deal of her immense personal energy to keeping Humpy under control as much as possible. However, after decades of trying to keep his rambunctious inner child from spinning out of orbit, she finally realized that in the long run, they are both happier if he just *did his own thing* while she tried to minimize the occasional fallout and blowback. She felt he needed an *organized outlet* for his constant mischief, and that is how the *Pirate's Barge* came into Humpy's hedonistic life.

For it came to pass that several years ago, Humpy discovered *the open road* as the most direct route to getting out from under Flynndra's diligent guardianship. He gathered up all of his loose change and made a considerable down-payment on a recreational vehicle of heretofore-unknown proportions regarding both physical stature and luxurious appointments. A fully self-contained playpen on six wheels. Proudly flying from the rear antenna was a pirate's skull and crossbones flag that the sainted Flynndra had made for him. Furthermore, to complete the pirate theme decor was a garish bumper sticker across the back door proclaiming, "Wenches ... prepare to be boarded!"

The *Pirate's Barge* was custom-built to Humpy's specifications based on Sigmund Freud's *Pleasure Principle.* It was set up to provide all the comforts of home, and more. It was *commodious,* as it even had a bathroom and a shower to provide for Humpy's comfort while he was out exploring the highways and byways of America for extended periods of time. Some of these road adventures could turn out to be great challenges, both from a physical endurance and a personal safety point of view.

The most recent near death-defying bout with wretched excess occurred when Humpy scheduled a visit to us here at Camp Kilbourne so that he and his faithful traveling companion, Baby Jaws Wilkins, could pay their respects as they piloted the *Pirate's Barge* northward to British Columbia on one of their historic road trips. I believe British Columbia was their ultimate destination, although

I did hear him mention New Zealand and then Tasmania at various points in a rambling explanation of their itinerary.

Humpy has a rambling, disjointed way of speaking that is not always easy to interpret. Whenever attempting to verbally communicate, the product of his effort was a signature stumbling, halting sort of syntax of such a quality and desperation that it is often mistaken for the speech pattern of a stroke victim. After all these years, I have been able to distill most of his incoherent requests down into two basic messages that go something like the following: Standard message #1, "Davie! Would ... you ... happen ... to ... have ... some ... drugs ... of ... a ... recreational ... nature ... that ... I ... could eat ... or ... maybe ... smoke?" Or, Standard message #2, "Davie! Do ... you happen ... to ... have ... any ... strong ... drink ... that ... I ... could ... borrow ... for ... just ... a ... few ... minutes?" He would then stare balefully with his watery blue eyes while wearing a maniacal grin. This would continue until I responded in some way or other that satisfied him.

Humpy dearly loved weddings and after a bottle or two of champagne he enjoyed giving his *special wedding toast to the Bride*. Over the course of his colorful adult years, he has been asked to leave no less than eight wedding receptions immediately following this bawdy performance. I recall once the bride's mother called the security guard to have him escorted off the property. I believe the toast went something like this:

Here's to the Bride! A dear friend whom I would like to toast! Of all the activities she seems to enjoy, she seems to enjoy drinking the most.

- *By the first drink she is becoming unstable*
- *By the second she is beginning to boast*
- *By the third drink she is under the table*
- *And by the fourth she is under the host!*

Whether he was on one of his famous road trips, or merely at home, Humpy is famous for losing most of the accessories that he employs to lend himself a bohemian look. A cornucopia of hats, scarves, and unorthodox footwear provide the basic building blocks for his *style*. Humpy is the only person I have ever known who could consistently lose just one shoe.

Road-tripping is not a casual activity with Humpy, and he places great importance on the gathering up and organizing of his *necessary supplies.* He uses the supply list of his alter ego whenever he was preparing for a trip that might last more than twenty-four hours. Unfortunately, his alter ego is the infamous Hunter S. Thompson. Therefore, the following direct excerpt from *Fear and Loathing in Las Vegas,* written by the late, great HST, would serve nicely as Humpy's typical basic supply list.

> *We were somewhere around Barstow on the edge of the desert when the drugs began to take hold. The trunk of the car looked like a police narcotics lab. We had two bags of grass, seventy-five pellets of mescaline, five sheets of high powered blotter acid, a salt shaker half-full of cocaine and a whole galaxy of multi-colored uppers, downers, screamers, laughers … and also a quart of tequila, a quart of rum, a case of Budweiser, a pint of raw ether and two dozen amyls.*

This description of necessary supplies would not be considered excessive by Humpy, although I believe he would require more tequila than HST apparently needed, and he would certainly upgrade the Budweiser listed by HST with Sierra Nevada Torpedo Extra IPA Ale, which boasts a husky 7.2 ABV.

On that fateful day that this story begins, I heard the *Pirate's Barge* laboring up the hill from several blocks away and knew that whatever hove into view next would be a compelling and memorable sight. Upon coming to an uncertain stop, Humpy clambered down from the cabin of the *Barge* amid a cacophonous clatter of cans and bottles. I was to later learn that a dental emergency provided the perfect excuse to indulge himself in excesses beyond the wildest imagination of mere mortals. Humpy's inner child was on the loose and out to play.

His traveling companion, Baby Jaws Wilkins, was also eager to get out of the *Pirate's Barge* and go pee in the bushes. After that she treated herself to a mighty excretion across the road, then went over and sociably sniffed our Bassett Hound Moose's nethers with great interest. Baby Jaws is a little bitch, or words to that effect. She is a female sort of dog of uncertain lineage and very fond of road trips.

Humpy had carefully scheduled his assault upon Camp Kilbourne to coincide with early vespers, which was just in time for a beer or two before we went to Sierra Nevada Brewery to benefit from whatever was new on tap there. I asked Humpy if he was okay since he looked more than a little under the weather, even for himself. He gleefully explained that he was suffering from a cracked crown on his right lower molar and was in considerable discomfort and was thereby cleared for self-medication, as required. He went on to say that for most of the day he had been diligently treating the condition with various combinations of pain retardants from the generous supply that was always near at hand during his road trips. I said that I might have a Vicodin around somewhere but he wouldn't want to take it while he was using alcohol. His response was, "Oh, I already took several of those bad boys. I'm going to soak the tooth in a tumbler of tequila for a few minutes to see if that provides any further relief." He soon finished off the tumbler of tequila and was ready to go to our excellent local brewery and try a few of their new releases.

And now we come to the most important aspect of this little story. While at the excellent Sierra Nevada Brewing Company, the finest brewery in all the land, I held forth at great length, with special emphasis, and in no uncertain terms, about the specific requirements of my personal schedule for the next day. This extraordinary effort in making things clear to Humpy was due to the fact that I had a long-awaited dinner date the following evening, and these plans had already been postponed once. Although Humpy usually only stayed overnight while visiting the Camp, depending on him to perform as expected, or required, was like depending on the weather when you have a big outdoor event to plan, such as the Kentucky Derby or WWII.

I made it abundantly clear that I would require a certain degree of privacy beginning the following afternoon, but I didn't think that would be a problem since he usually departed the Camp on the first tide. He assured me not to worry, that this would also be the case on this visit. I asked about his dental emergency, in an attempt to find out if he had plans to have that looked into before he left Chico. He said that no, he would get that taken care of *on up the road*. I said that if he changed his mind, we would certainly want to get an early dental appointment so he could still stay on our mutually agreed upon schedule. I don't think he heard a lot of this as his level of awareness was severely compromised by the various chemical compounds that he had ingested within the past few hours.

After sampling several newly released ales at the Sierra Nevada Taproom, we returned to the Camp where it was feeding time for my teenage daughter, Savannah A. Kilbourne, the finest daughter in all the land. Savannah wanted to know what was wrong with *Uncle Humpy* as he seemed to be very glassy eyed and was mumbling and humming something about taquitos and tequila. I answered that he wasn't feeling so good after all the aspirin he had taken for his toothache.

Humpy energetically addressed himself to a heaping plate of taquitos and beans, all of which he washed down with several iced *cervesas*. The numerous Vicodins must have kicked in nicely as he seemed to have no trouble chewing with his sore tooth. After eating this enormous dinner, he promptly lapsed into a deep sleep while still at the table. I asked Savannah for her help in getting Humpy out of the house and into the *Barge*, as he was *very sleepy* after having just completed such a long and painful day of driving.

The next morning arrived right on schedule, and after returning from taking Savannah to school, I began the challenge of bringing Humpy back to consciousness so that he could begin his considerable preparations before leaving on what now looked to be the second tide. When he did finally come out of the *Pirate's Barge* and into the house, he looked much the worse for wear and casually remarked that he had changed his mind and now planned to stay an extra day. He wanted to have his tooth treated before he left on the major leg of his trip to British Columbia, or New Zealand or Tasmania, or wherever the roads took him.

I had a major OMG moment and sternly reminded him of our numerous conversations about this very issue all the way up until he lapsed into his deep slumber last night. He agreed that he *remembered something about all that* but still felt that another day would be required before he was able to continue. He mentioned that he "had eaten a lot of Vicodin and could still feel some pain in the tooth." He went on to say, however, that he didn't seem to have any pain, or any feeling at all, anywhere else from his neck to his toes. He seemed very casual about his schedule, which, as mentioned above, was in no way casual with me as it was based upon a highly anticipated dinner event here at the Camp that had already been postponed once.

With this possible heartbreak looming, I was highly motivated to find some immediate dental care that would allow Humpy to be on his way by early afternoon, or sooner if possible. I told him to go on back to bed and to cease and desist with the Vicodin. I would begin calling local dentists to see who could take him in on an emergency basis. He said that it would be great if I wanted to be the dental emergency coordinator and that he considered myself to be *his guardian* in this case. It became painfully clear what trials and tribulations the sainted Flynndra had been going through all these years. Humpy then availed himself of a large smoldering bowl of controversial medicinal herbs and then, with a mischievous wink, retired back into the depth of the *Pirate's Barge*.

I called my dentist first and was told that Humpy could be seen the following week. I asked if they knew of an office that could see him that morning, and they referred me to a dentist they thought might be available. I called that office forthwith and was told that Dr. Long-Gone was on vacation, but I might try a Dr. May-Be-In-Town to see if I could set up an appointment there.

By this time desperation was beginning to set in, and I had phone directories strewn throughout the room. After several more calls, I finally found an office that had an early cancellation and could see him at 10:00, if I could get him there by then. That was in a mere thirty minutes, but I was determined to make this happen. I went outside and got Humpy back up again and told him to get dressed ASAP. I had no idea where Dr. Bring-Him-On-In's dental office was so I had to factor in time to get lost on the way. Humpy didn't seem to be fully conscious but said he would make an effort. He just wanted to put a little more tequila on the tooth first.

I assumed he would be at the dental office for some time, and since I had a very busy schedule throughout the rest of the day, I had him follow me in the *Pirate's Barge*. I had gone no more than three blocks when I checked the rearview mirror and could see no sign of the *Barge*. I dashed back home to find Humpy still laboriously backing out of the driveway with a perplexed look on his face, as if he were wondering where I had disappeared. He was operating in ultra-slow motion. He was on Vicodin time.

We finally got our two vehicles coordinated and in line, one behind the other, and were on the way to the dentist's office. Mercifully,

I was able to find it without wasting too much time on being lost. I got Humpy parked while I went in to warn the office staff of the situation they were about to face. I then went out and retrieved Humpy, and taking him firmly by the arm, led him into the office and graciously introduced him to the receptionist. I said, "This patient's name is Humpy Wilkins. He is not from around here. He is ready for treatment and has generous insurance. I am his Guardian. Do I need to sign anything before you begin? You will not need to use any anesthesia on him. Please call me and let me know how everything goes. Goodbye."

I then beat a hasty retreat back to the Camp where I had business to take care of. I assumed that I wouldn't hear back from the dentist's office for an hour or so. However the dreaded call came much sooner than that. They had X-rayed his molar and it was clear that it was cracked right down to the root and in need of some major care.

Dr. Bring-Him-On-In reported that he had informed Humpy that there were three options available to him. One was to begin a program that would ultimately result in his having a jaw reconstruction and dental implant. This would take seven to eight separate visits over a period of six to eight months and would cost approximately $400,000 or about the same amount as one year at Stanford University on the economy plan. The second option, and the one strongly doctor-recommended, would be to make a temporary crown for the tooth today and then come back *in several days* when the permanent crown would be installed. This would cost approximately $3,500. I was reluctantly told that the third option would be to "do an extraction, which is pretty much unheard of in the dental profession these days." The cost of that service would be limited to $100 since they probably wouldn't need to give him any anesthesia, and in fact would refuse to administer any to him in his present condition.

Dr. Bring-Him-On-In went on to comment with concern that Humpy seemed to be very groggy and wasn't able to carry on a meaningful conversation about the three options available to him. Humpy had asked that I be called and consulted since I was his guardian and he trusted me with his very life. "Call Davie and he'll take care of this decision-making business for us, as I trust him with my very life" I was told were his exact words. I could see my dinner date plans taking wing; therefore, as a mere flesh and blood mortal, I impulsively shouted to Dr. Bring-Him-On-In to "Just put him down!" I told him that under the circumstances, and considering Humpy's advanced age, his chronic incontinence and probable liver condition as well as his many dead brain cells, it would be a merciful decision to euthanize him, to put him out of his misery and pain. It would be the humane thing to do.

Dr. Bring-Him-On-In asked what I meant by that, exactly, and I said, "Well, did you ever read Steinbeck's *Of Mice and Men?* Do you recall what had to be done with poor old Lenny? Well, I mean, put him down like that. You are George and he is Lenny." The reluctant Doctor asked, "Well, what about his family?" I responded that Humpy was an orphan and a child of the road with no ties that I knew of. No one would ever have to know what happened, and he could charge for the full crown if he wanted to. In retrospect, I now understand that perhaps *putting him down* wasn't the nicest thing to suggest, but I was stressed out and my patience was being put to a great test.

Anyway, it was a non-issue since the narrow-minded and unimaginative Dr. Uptight-Panties-In-A-Wad told me that I must be kidding. He said that he didn't run a SPCA euthanasia service out of his office. What an inconsiderate wimp! With his unfortunate limitation of services in mind, I then said, "Well, what the hail then, just separate that molar from his head, give him a little pat on the butt and send him on his way, Stat!"

Dr. Boring-And-Unimaginative mentioned that it had been some time since they had done an extraction but if I was sure that this was my decision acting as his guardian, then they would proceed with the operation. I said go for it, as I had a busy social schedule and needed to get Humpy on the road to Tasmania, or wherever, as soon as possible. He went on to say that they weren't comfortable extracting the tooth and having him leave the office without my being there to take charge of him. I said to just let him sleep for an hour or so back in their supply room, or somewhere, and then he would be fine. But it didn't work out that way. Humpy was to have an Es Cape.

Meanwhile, back at the Camp, I still nurtured strong hopes that Humpy would be all right to continue on his trip that afternoon when he got back from the dentist's office. I spent a restless afternoon pacing up and down the driveway while trying to contact him. He was way overdue and the dinner date clock was ticking. I called his cell phone numerous times but had no luck getting through to him. Finally, in desperation, I called the dentist's office and asked for a report on what had happened to Humpy after the procedure. Nurse Truly-Shocked-And-Amazed said that she was truly shocked and amazed to hear from me and said that he had been gone from their office for over three hours.

They had left him on a couch in the break room and when they checked up on him a few minutes later, he was missing. He had gone out the back door without a trace except for a pile of bloody gauze packets. It looked, she said, like someone had been brutally murdered back there. I responded ominously that this could only mean one thing: He had gone down the rabbit hole and into his own private parallel universe! Call the authorities!

I quickly put out an all points bulletin for Humpy. I called several bars and half a dozen known local drug dealers. I also had friends go by Sierra Nevada to see if he had somehow washed up on their sudsy shore. No sightings were made. I then made the call I had been hoping to avoid all day long. I called my lady friend and again postponed our dinner date. I explained that Humpy had

made an Es Cape and was lost somewhere between Chico and Tasmania and I had to find him. I also mentioned that he was missing
a major molar that he had been very attached to and might not be
aware of that fact yet.

After all hope for the dinner date was abandoned, and approximately four hours after he escaped from the dentist's office, Humpy
came touring up in the *Pirate's Barge* as if he had merely driven down
to the corner grocery for a quart of beer. By now it was late afternoon
and he had spent the past four hours medicating himself while attempting to overcome what he referred to as *the horror* that had
happened to him after I had abandoned him at the dentist's office.
He never brought up the awkward euthanasia issue, so I guess that conversation between himself and Dr. Party-Pooper had not occurred. This
was probably a good thing. He found himself to be very thirsty and was
starving for a large portion of rare beef. He was also obsessed with
showing us the gigantic empty socket where his molar had been located for the past six decades.

He then proceeded to open a bottle of thick red wine as he felt
this was the most direct route to replacing the copious amount of
blood that he had shed during the horror of the extraction. He
commented that he must have dozed off in the dentist's chair, as he
was very surprised when they woke him up and showed him his
large and gory molar. However, he was pleased that the entire
process, which he seemed to have missed, had only cost him $100.
Plus he had been given a new prescription for Vicodin as a bonus.
And as a souvenir, he was given his large, gory molar which contained both a big crack and a small gold filling. He said he planned
to make a watch fob out of it.

I inquired as to where he had been for the past half-day and his answer was, *Oh, just here and there.* After more specific questioning, I
found out that he had *gone shopping* for a new supply of tequila and a
six-pound tri tip roast. He had also found a pharmacy to fill his new

prescription for Vicodin and then stopped in at a downtown neighborhood bar for a game of shuffleboard and a couple of beers. He hadn't been able to find his way back to the Sierra Nevada Taproom. After that, he went to the park and took a nap.

While Humpy proceeded to BBQ the haunch of beef, I prepared a salad, baked potatoes, and some garlic bread, all of which was intended to be prepared for and eaten by my lady friend and myself that very same evening. Again, as had occurred the previous evening, Humpy devoured enough food to feed a small African village. He then announced that he was going out to take Baby Jaws for a post-prandial walk.

Savannah and I cleaned up the kitchen, did the dishes and then watched a full-length movie before she wondered out loud whatever had happened to *Uncle Humpy*. It occurred to me that he had been out walking Baby Jaws for nearly three hours and perhaps I should go out and check up on him.

I found Humpy sitting upright behind the wheel of the *Pirate's Barge*, enjoying the healthful benefits of a deep slumber. Baby Jaws looked as though she had been walked so I tried to relocate Humpy out of the cab and into the commodious interior. He refused my kind offer of assistance. When I later checked up on him, around 3:00 A.M. he was still in situ, *sleeping the sleep of the innocent*, deep in the arms of Morpheus.

Again, morning arrived right on time, and following my return from taking Savannah to school, I discovered that Humpy was ambulatory and seemingly refreshed. He had ignited his early morning bowl of controversial medicinal herbs and seemed to be enjoying a miraculous recovery from the previous day's horror that had been wrought upon him by the dreaded Dr. Bring-Him-On-Over. I would have admitted myself to the emergency room of the local hospital if I had suffered the ordeals that he had visited upon his own personal body in the past twenty-four hours.

He did seem to be curious about the deep hole that he discovered in his mouth where the molar had once been. He said that he intended to keep the empty socket filled with tequila. After an hour or so of self-medication and several cups of espresso, he began to make motions that would cause a person to think he might actually be preparing to depart. Baby Jaws was given a walk and then reattached to the bumper of the *Pirate's Barge* where she was always kept when she wasn't out prowling the neighborhood seeking cats to eat.

Things seemed to be moving in the right direction. I suggested to Humpy that he do a careful walk-through in the house to see what he might be leaving behind, as usual. After a cursory glance through the house, he came back out with one of my books, *The Complete Idiot's Guide to Self-Medication*, which he intended to borrow. We then shook hands all around, both of us together, and did the usual backslaps for a few minutes after which he climbed heroically up into the control center of the *Pirate's Barge* and declared himself fit to resume his road adventure to British Columbia or Tasmania, or wherever. He fired up the mighty diesel engine and with a jaunty salute and a roguish wink, began slowly backing down the driveway.

I asked him where Baby Jaws was and he replied that she was in the back cabin where she would travel in luxurious comfort while he toiled over the controls at freeway speeds. I asked again if he was sure she was safely stored in the back of the *Pirate's Barge* and he said, "Oh yeah, that's where she likes to ride." I suggested that maybe he should just give one last check to make sure she was all set to go before he got out on the road that ran along the front of our property. He finally dismounted from the cab of the *Barge* to give one last check whereupon he almost stumbled over Baby Jaws, who was still securely attached to the bumper with her steel cable.

Humpy exclaimed, "Oh my God! She would have to run really fast if she was going to keep up once I hit the freeway!" Luckily, I had noticed her predicament so knew she wasn't in any great danger. She did, however, seem relieved to get into the *Barge* before it began backing down the driveway. With Baby Jaws safely inside, Humpy departed for destinations known to no man.

Later that morning, as I was cleaning up the random debris from Humpy's visit, I found his favorite "Bubba's BBQ and Boiled Peanuts Emporium" hat and two shoes, one an electric blue running shoe and one a pointy-toe alligator pump. Not surprisingly, the shoes didn't relate in any way except they were both for the right foot. I envisioned him driving down the freeway wearing one blue running shoe and one fancy dress alligator pump. The left ones.

Note: Let it be known that this is a heavily fictionalized account of a real event. Specific details are not intended to offend anyone whose name might be Humpy, Uncle Humpy, Humbert J. Wilkins, Baby Jaws or Mr. Wilkins, or any other person, living or dead, whoever and wherever they might be.

This is no cow steak! I discovered too late that this is actually a four-pound blackened catfish or, "Ze poisson chat noirci, grande!" as that great dildo flamer, Pierre Nolastname would say. Note bottle of Sierra Nevada Torpedo Strong Ale, which saved the day.

The Story of Jinks Malloy or How I Once Ate An Entire Four-Pound Blackened Catfish, Mostly by Accident

I VIVIDLY RECALL THAT FATEFUL EVENING some years ago when I first met Jinks Malloy. What happened was that I was all-alone by myself that weekend and somehow found myself inside the Old Navy Inn, which was a classic Chico neighborhood bar but should not be considered a dive. The Old Navy Inn served actual food and offered an actual menu including corndogs and deep-fried potatoes. The Old Navy Inn also served fish tacos, which were of no use to me as eating fish gives me the howling skitters. On the other hand, dive bars only offer two items of food on their menu, pickled pig's feet and hard-boiled eggs. I don't personally use your chicken eggs because I know where they come out of when they exit the chicken.

But I digress. As I walked into the Old Navy Inn, I immediately spotted herself from across the crowded room. I remember there was an old Frank Sinatra song playing on the jukebox. I believe it was *The Summer Wind.* Our eyes met with a flash of electricity. I became lightheaded and disoriented for a brief moment, perhaps because of the four-day-old pulled pork sandwich I had eaten for breakfast. Magic was loose upon the land while scenes from *Casablanca* flickered in the archives of my memory.

She was willowy and stylish and pleasant to look upon. She was the sort of woman the British are fond of saying was *very nicely put together.* In other words, she was easy on the eyes. Even though she was a voluptuous sort of woman, she appeared to still have all her original parts with no replacements or surgical refurbishment. She was a green-eyed and blonde-haired sort of woman. Eye-catching was the word.

This woman strongly reminded me of a fabulously beautiful woman I had a hectic relationship with several jumps back. That woman was a Yankee woman, as she was from upstate New York. She was from Troy, New York, to be exact. Although her full and formal name was Helen Marie Potter, I simply referred to her as *Helen of Troy*. She was straight out of Homer's *Iliad*. She possessed crystal blue eyes, wrinkly strawberry blonde hair and a voice that sounded like perfectly tuned wind chimes. She had a dusting of freckles and the sexiest ankles I had ever witnessed. Like the original Helen of Troy, Helen *from* Troy's face could launch a thousand ships, even on a bad hair day, which she never had.

From talking to the barkeep, which was highly instructive, I learned the eye-catching woman was something of a regular at the Old Navy Inn and that her drink of choice was champagne. She was a champagne-drinking sort of woman! Her name was Jinks Malloy. Sheer name-poetry to my ears. I sidled up to her, and with a pronounced inhalation gently exclaimed, "Girl! You smell good! You smell like you just took a bath in rainbows and cupcakes!" She actually smelled like a combination of White Shoulders and cigar. She gave forth with a mighty eye roll and asked if that lame pickup line had ever worked for me before. I had to admit that one time when I used that line, it caused me to end up being married. I mentioned that I used it with extreme caution since then.

We spoke in an informed way about the healthful benefits of champagne for a while, and then she asked whether I would mind if she smoked. I opined that it would be okay as long as she didn't exhale on me. At that point she gave forth with a devilish smile, and reaching down into her little sequined *going to the prom* purse, withdrew a package of smallish cigars. She was a cigar-smoking sort of woman! We sampled several varieties and brands of champagne while she demurely smoked her little wooden-tipped Hav-A-Tampa. She didn't inhale, much like Bill Clinton.

Events progressed apace as we passed a pleasant several hours. However, before another hour had passed, while I reminisced about my childhood on Pawleys Island and my traumatic connection with the fish, she informed me that she had to go home and finish her packing. She sadly explained that she was relocating over the weekend down to Laguna Beach, where she had been hired as a professional model.

I carefully explained that I thought Laguna Beach was in the neighboring state of Southern California and was located hundreds of miles away. I asked her if she was aware of that fact. She admitted that she was and suggested that I might wish to come down and visit her sometime. At that point we exchanged information vital to any ongoing communication between ourselves, then she left the Old Navy Inn for the last time. Both the barkeep and I were very sad to see her go. At that point she was a long-gone sort of woman. I couldn't get the lovely and mysterious Jinks Malloy out of my mind, so from time to time I would send her a picture postcard of the front of the Old Navy Inn. I had hopes that she might become sentimental and find cause to return to Chico where I languished without her.

Her response was always the same. "You are such a sweetheart! Come on down to Southern California for a visit. I believe I could make your trip worth the effort." A few picture postcards later, she explained that she now had a wonderful studio apartment, which was situated immediately over a five-star seafood restaurant on the Pacific Coast Highway. This wide, tree-lined avenue traversed the heart of Laguna Beach nightlife with its various and sundry bars and restaurants. She may have mentioned that she would like to have dinner there. She also said, "You can stay over with me if you want." Two details, *studio apartment* and *you can stay with me if you want*, especially resonated with me. Her comment about the apartment being over an excellent seafood restaurant didn't register somehow. Being a man of action, I booked a flight for the coming weekend.

As I was on my flight to LAX, the fact that her apartment was directly above a five-star seafood restaurant began to haunt me. For it was during my formative years while growing up on Pawleys Island that I lived among the fish-eaters and was force-fed so many mullet that my personal DNA was nearly the same as the mullet's for several years. When we moved away from Pawleys Island, I swore I would never eat another fish during this lifetime. Fish gave me the skittering whim-whams.

Yet it came to pass that on a balmy Friday afternoon I flew into the Los Angeles Airport with *Fish Anxiety Syndrome* (simply referred to as FAS in most clinical psychology texts) beginning to take root in my stomach's early warning system. After some negotiating with the car rental people, I was issued a little silver rental car with a retractable cloth top. Following some time spent becoming lost, twice, I located her address on the Pacific Coast Highway, a cozy little love nest right above the *Maison de le Francoise de Mer.* Whatever that meant. Some foreign language or other.

While on the flight I had looked up the restaurant in the *AAA Tourbook,* and learned that it was categorized as *Upscale French.* Apparently this was not one of those *all you can eat for $4.95* buffets that I was fond of. The additional description suggested that the hopeful diner would require reservations and would want to be dressed in *smart dining attire.* It went on to say that the Maison de le Francoise de Mer was *all the buzz* with the Laguna Beach in-crowd. It enjoyed a five-star rating, therefore seating on the weekends was very much in demand. The message was loud and clear: Bring a fat new credit card, dress up, and prepare to be disrespected in French.

When I arrived in front of the *Mason de la Frances the Mare,* or whatever, I called Jinks on my little car phone to let her know I was downstairs. She opened the window above the sidewalk and beckoned me to come on up. She looked delicious, which caused visions of sugarplums to dance in my head. She met me at the door with a bottle of cold champagne. It had to be five o'clock somewhere.

After some small talk, I asked where I should put my overnight bag. I swear she said, "Oh, just by the bed there. No, not this side, the other side. This is my side, silly." Once I managed to get control of my pulse rate and blood pressure, I exclaimed how glad I was to be there with her and how much fun we were going to have with ourselves, all together. Jinks went on to say how much she was looking forward to our dinner downstairs at the Maison de le Francoise de Mer, or something like that. We finished the champagne and changed into our *smart and trendy* dinner clothes and then proceeded to make our way downstairs where Jinks had reserved us a premium table by the fireplace.

We were met at the door by a very supercilious individual with a saccharine smile and a pencil-thin black moustache. He looked like the evil guy who always tied the innocent young damsel in distress to the train tracks. His hair was all black and styled in the fashion of an Elvis Presley pompadour. It looked like he kept it in place with chicken grease or something. He was dressed all in starch and was unnaturally stiff except in his wrist bones, which hung limply as he waved his arms all around with great dramatic effect. He seated us with an exaggerated flourish and exclaimed, "Mademoiselle Jinks, Oh Oui! So magnifique this very night! So feminine, so chic! Oh, oui, oui!" Mademoiselle Jinks gave forth with a blush and shy smile and introduced me to this person whose name, of course, was Pierre. Just Pierre, no last name. His last name should have been Unctuous. Mr. Pierre Unctuous. She went on to say, "Pierre, this is my friend David who is visiting me this weekend."

Pierre gushed and spittled all over me while saying, "Ah Monsieur Daveed! Will you be visiting the delicious Mademoiselle Jinks this night, no?" I turned to Jinks and said, "What did he just say? Did he just insult you?" Jinks replied, "He wants to know if you are visiting me, I guess." I tried to get back on track with this obnoxious European person by saying, "So Pierre, what do you have to eat here in this restaurant tonight?" I cleverly followed that comment up with, "Are you a flamer or what, because you sure act like one." Jinks threw me a look of strong disapproval while mentioning that she thought Pierre *talked pretty*. At that point I realized that I had to stay on my best behavior, at least until we got back upstairs.

I engaged in friendly discourse with the limp-wristed Pierre by explaining the obvious to him. "Now look here, Pierre, I'm a red-blooded American and I need a large steak, medium rare because I have a lot of work ahead of me tonight." Wink, Wink. That comment caused the lovely Mademoiselle to blush prettily. I then pointed to the table next to ours and asked, "What is that over there on that plate? Is that a steak?" Pierre responded with an enthusiastic eye roll and exclaimed, "Oh oui! oui! Eet is le especial de le maison! Ah, how do we say to you, the poisson chat noirci, grande! Oui … oui … eet es le incredi-a-ble! Much grande!! Oui … oui. Ze spe'cial de le maison! We only just have two left this night, Monsieur Daveed. Do you wish?"

I asked back, "But is it a steak or what?" I thought it looked kind of suspicious. I had my glasses off so I could impress Mademoiselle Jinks with my sincere and trustworthy look that says, "I need to be nurtured, please" and couldn't see the next-door table in very clear detail. Pierre rolled his eyes again and gushed, "Oh oui oui, le steak of le mer grande … no?" I wasn't too keen on all the oui, oui stuff but said, "Okay, if that's a grande steak, from the beef, you know, the cow? Moo! I'll have it medium rare. Grande is okay. And bring some more of that champagne for the Mademoiselle."

Pierre disappeared with a swish and soon more champagne arrived. The tempo began to settle down at our little premium table by the fireplace now that Pierre was off harassing some other American couple. I mentioned that I thought Pierre was tres affected and probably wasn't even from France. He might have been from Compton or somewhere else in the bowels of Southern California. Jinks said that Pierre was probably *just sensitive* and I should be extra nice to him.

She explained that back in her college days, she had waited tables to pay her way through school and learned that it was always extremely important to support and encourage the waiters. She went on to say that often waiters were the more sensitive types, especially these French waiters. I said that I couldn't agree more and explained that I always got along very well with those folks of foreign extraction. At that time I would have agreed that yes, I would go jump in the ocean, had she suggested that I go for a long stroll off a short pier. I was eager to please the lovely Mademoiselle and ready to make nice with the waiters, even if they weren't Americans or members of the United States citizenry.

I had to admit, however, that my experience with French people–that is, those folks from the country of France–was limited. I knew they invented the deep-fried potato, the French dressing, and a special kind of kissing, and I deeply appreciated that.

We passed a pleasant half-hour like that, drinking champagne and getting mellow. The lovely Ms. Malloy, AKA Madame Wozel la Tres Chic, etc. looked so … how did that dildo Pierre say it? "Madame Wetzel La Magnifique," or something like that. I said I had an idea of what I wanted for dessert. She favored me with a sweet smile and a little eye-roll.

Suddenly, from the back of the restaurant there arose such a clatter that I looked to the kitchen to see what was the matter, and who should appear so bustling and quick but that great French nimrod Pierre with two helpers right behind. He is beaming and rolling his eyes for all he's worth. What a showoff. He is carrying a large oval covered dish up above his head with one hand while waving the other one, the one with the broken wrist, around like he's swatting flies off a week-old ripe mullet. I'm thinking, oh yeah, that looks like a grande piece of beef for sure. He was straining under the weight of the covered charger and beginning to perspire profusely. A large chunk of his slicked-back pompadour had come loose and was threatening to flop down over his eyes and blind him.

With a mighty flourish, he swept the table clean and placed the gigantic covered charger directly in front of me with a huge swish and says, "Zot Alours! Ze spe'cial de le maison for my lovely new fran, Monsieur Daveed! Ze poisson chat noirci, grande! Woot! Woot!" He was not using his inside voice. Pierre was fast losing control and in need of a serious time-out.

With that said, he whipped the cover off the large oval serving dish, and where my Grande Medium Rare Side of Beef should have been, there was a gigantic dead and blackened catfish! With the head, whiskers, and tail still attached! With the two dead catfish eyes blindly staring at me. I jumped to my feet and threw the sign of the hex at the catfish. Forefingers crossed and facing the devil's spawn, I shouted, "Stand back everyone! Where is my steak, my cow meat...you know, moo!" Pierre said "Oh, we thought you to be making ze joke, you know poisson mean fish en France, no? This es le seafood restaurant. We do not haf ze steak, how do you say et, ze moo."

Mademoiselle Jinks was also in shock because of the tragic nature of the moment, although she seemed to regain her social equilibrium much sooner than I did. She said, "Oh, don't worry, Pierre, Monsieur Daveed will eat it, and I'm sure he will enjoy it." She flared her eyes, and nostrils, at me as if to say that I was embarrassing this poor sensitive French flamer and I had better make it up to Pierre by eating every last bite of that four-pound blackened catfish with a smile. She sternly warned that I would get no dessert until I had finished all of my dinner.

I calmly ordered a full quart of Sierra Nevada's Best Torpedo Extra Special India Pale Ale, with an aggressive ABV of seven-point-two alcohol by volume. Then, putting my mind back in my happy place–sitting at the bar of the Sierra Nevada Taproom in Chico, in the great state of Northern California, with my faithful Thursday Evening Crew–I dutifully ate my four-pound blackened catfish all gone. I even ate the elbow, whatever that was.

The horrendous trauma of this fish-eating experience was later mitigated when the lovely Jinks served dessert. As the late Maurice Sendak would say, "It was a wild rumpus!" The reward was well worth the effort.

PART SEVEN

MODERN MIRACLES!

One of very few known published pictures of Uncle Bubba's Electronified Pork Pulling Machine, A Modern Miracle (Pat. pend.). This unique item of Southern cooking equipment was originally designed by a Mr. Ruben "Rube" Goldberg, of Aiken, South Carolina. This copper-clad pork-rendering device could easily convert a 100 lb. shoat into 200 one-half pound pulled pork sandwiches in just under seven minutes. However, Uncle Bubba admitted that cleaning the unit could be laborious. He had wheels built on the unit so he could drive it through the carwash from time to time. The young hog was vacuumed up into a compartment built into the base of the unit and the "Bubba's Big Boy" one half-pound sandwiches were propelled from the 8" tube at the rear. Much of the device was for show and he ordered it built at the Acme Steampunk Factory with several extra bells, whistles, pulleys and levers, as well as a police siren and flashing lights. He occasionally entered it into the Miss Pulled Pork Festival parade, which was a popular annual event in historic George-town, South Carolina. Photo courtesy Alex-Holden.

Uncle Bubba's Electronified Pork-Pulling Machine, A Modern Miracle!

"If it had grown up," she said to herself, "it would have made a dreadfully ugly child; but it makes a rather handsome pig I think."
Alice's Adventures in Wonderland

During my lifetime I have spent considerable time and energy, and fossil fuels, searching for the perfect Southern pulled pork BBQ. In fact, I was once given a shirt with the phrase, *Pigs quiver when they hear my name.* Indeed, a pig I once owned did exactly that, but that's another story.

Early on during this time of intense study, I learned there were important differences between the pulled pork of various Carolina regions. The three main pork categories that I have studied are 1) pulled, 2) chopped, and 3) ruined. Anything reduced further than chopped tends to be more of a hash substance and is best consumed by North Carolinians, a confused people who have never gotten their pork BBQ priorities sorted out.

While carrying out this life's work, I also learned there are marked regional differences in the sort of BBQ sauce that aficionados prefer on their pork. There is the very fine mustard-based sauce and then a sort of okay tomato-based sauce, and then there is the not-at-all-okay vinegar-based sauce favored by those same North Carolinians who enjoy their BBQ pork chopped and ruined. It should be made clear there is a little vinegar in all BBQ pork sauces, but it needs to know its place. First is the mustard, then the brown sugar, and last, and least, is a little dash of apple cider vinegar.

During this decades-long odyssey, I have encountered a wide assortment of memorable BBQ restaurant names. A tasteful sampling of these names follows:

Little Big Al's Chopped Hash and Snouts BBQ
Willie Mae's Pork BBQ and Social Club
Big Boy's Fried Pies and Pulled Pork
Ham Bone's Stoppin' Place
Piggy Palace BBQ and Used Cars Shop
Frenchie's Mexican Restaurant and BBQ
Big Foot's Pork Paradise and Strong Ale Taproom
    and last but not least,
Bubba's Pulled Pork and Boiled Peanuts Emporium

Bubba's proudly displays a sign stating, *Our BBQ is from pigs that made perfect hogs of themselves.* Note to readers: Bubba is a very common name among the good ol' boys of the south. All Bubbas generally have a similar personal shape, which is best described as *husky.* As in, "That Bubba was a husky ol' boy who could sure eat himself some lard cakes and chitterlings. Too bad his heart attacked him at such a young age."

On a more positive note, it should be reported that, in my considerable experience, Aiken County, South Carolina has more five-star BBQ restaurants than any other region of the Palmetto State. Restaurants in this sand hills sector of South Carolina typically feature a pulled pork style with a more coarse texture that is served with a fine mustard-based sauce.

Southern BBQ restaurant menus often provide a spiritual feeling. For example, Carolina BBQ has a printed menu featuring this church ad: *Join us for worship this Sunday at Cornith Baptist Church in New Ellington, S.C.* while the Heavenly Hog BBQ Restaurant menu offers a discount to local churchgoers. *Show church bulletin and get 10 percent off meal. Sundays only.*

Uncle Bubba's famous flying pig. Almost an exact replica of my late pet pig, Barker, aka, Little Mr. Pulled Pork Sandwich. Notice this pig has all four legs which is unusual for a tender and tasty porker of this size. I call dibs on the wings.

The best kind of BBQ restaurant offers its food buffet-style rather than the more standard table service-style of most restaurants. In a good buffet-style BBQ restaurant, there may be twenty or more items available to the diner. However, only three of these items will earn my attention. First there is the pulled pork bin that may or may not be *pre-sauced.* Then there is the cole slaw bin, which gets my secondary attention.

Lastly, there is the cornbread tray, which may be loaded with either fluffy or flat bread, somewhat dependent on the amount of lard used in the recipe. I am especially fond of the flatter, more dense corn bread, such as is offered at Big D's Bar-B-Q Barn near Myrtle Beach, South Carolina. It has been my experience to observe that our Yankee-American brothers and sisters most often prefer their cornbread to be fluffy while loyal members of the Confederate States prefer the more dense and flat cornbread, which is widely acknowledged to be more authentic and civilized.

I spoke at length with Big D himself regarding the exquisite nature of their more dense corn bread. Mr. Big D gravely made the following deeply philosophical statement concerning this very issue when he said, "It's all in the lard, son, it's all in the lard." I can only guess they must use a flatter, more dense sort of lard there at Big D's. That is some fine eating lard!

If the diner is lucky, they might find a hushpuppy or corndodger tray instead of the cornbread tray. There is an important distinction between hush puppies, which includes a little onion, and corndodgers, which have a sweeter flavor coming from a traditional southern *Johnny Cake* heritage. I am led to understand that the term *Johnny Cake* was first used during the War Between the States when the brave and good southern soldiers were referred to as *Johnny Rebs*. There was a song that included the line, *When Johnny comes marching home again* …. The intention was to serve them cakes and 'shine until they could not remember the details of their service to the South.

In keeping with this historic naming of these good corn products, I am also led to understand that hush puppies were invented by early southern plantation owners as a means of keeping their coon hounds quiet as they crept up on the wily raccoon or o'possum that was wisely up a tree. Hence the term *hush puppy*. The hunters would toss the hush puppies to their hounds, and while the coon dogs were busily eating the delicious treats, the hunters would have themselves a slash of the corn liquor jug that was being passed around. Unfortunately, the wise old coon usually made his escape while all this fellowship was going on below.

But I digress. Once upon a time I ate so many corndodgers that, upon my departure, the restaurant owner was heard to comment, "Well, there goes Dodger Stadium." Sweet tea is also a necessary ingredient of the genuine pulled pork experience. This all-you-can-drink beverage will usually cost one American dollar. I generally require merely one quart while your genuine Bubba would require no less than one gallon of this sugary elixir.

As was mentioned earlier, the texture of BBQ pork is extremely important and ranges from pulled to chopped to all ground up, which is another term for *ruined*. Furthermore, there is a distinction between hand-pulled and machine-pulled. My worthy friend Bubba, who is Big D's number three offspring, recently invented his famous *electronified pork-pulling machine* which can be calibrated from a fine texture to a more chunky texture, or anywhere in between. However, there is no setting on his machine for *ruined*, which would be popular with our brothers and sisters next door in the neighboring state of North Carolina. As I said, those misguided Northern Carolinians eat their BBQ all ground up with a thin vinegar-based sauce.

In my BBQ travels throughout the South, I often carry a plastic shower curtain with me as a means of protecting my clothing and self while dealing with an especially frisky plate of pulled pork with extra mustard sauce. I find that the use of a nice tarp or shower curtain lends a certain note of elegance to the pulled pork dining experience. Also, when it is known in advance that I'm on the hunt for the wily pulled pork, several of my target restaurants ask for a three-day notification prior to my arrival to assure that an adequate supply of pulled pork be available to meet my requirements.

Someday I would like to be the proprietor of a genuine Southern Pulled Pork BBQ Restaurant. My business would include several quality pool tables, a generous selection of microbrew products on tap, such as Sierra Nevada's finest *Love Potion No. 69 Strong Ale*, and a kitchen producing nothing but authentic Southern Pulled Pork BBQ. The name of this restaurant would most assuredly be *Bubba Dave's Billiards, Brews and BBQ*. This says it all to me.

Behold the storied Woogie Snatcher! Note carved alligator which lends air of authenticity. This special two-handed Model LP69 design can actually snatch up to five woogies at one fell swoop. Also sturdy enough to serve as redheaded stepchild behavior reinforcement tool.

The Invention of the Woogie Snatcher!

I HAVE ALWAYS BEEN DEEPLY TROUBLED BY CHICKEN EGGS. When I was nine and being raised up in the great state of South Carolina, I owned a small flock of pet chickens. They were pets because each had an individual, personalized pet chicken name, and we only ate their eggs, not the chickens themselves. Unfortunately, purely by accident, I once looked too closely at a broken-open egg and saw that whitish, wormish-looking thing that is attached to the chicken egg yolk. My dear friend and close neighbor, Marlene Updagrove, who was ten at the time and very well informed on the topic of the birds and the bees, told me that the wormish-looking thing was the rooster's sperm and was not safe to eat. She told me that she was very careful to take the white thing out of her eggs because she didn't want to start laying any eggs herself. Ever since I was told that the ugly whitish thing was actually rooster sperm, I have not been able to eat eggs comfortably. I have named that spermish-looking thing the egg's *belly button,* and it must be completely removed before I can eat the egg itself. The removal of the *belly button* is always a tricky operation as it clings to the yolk with great tenacity. When you finally do get it loose, it slips off the fork, or whatever implement you are employing in your attempt to remove it.

One day a friend was over for breakfast and observed my labors to remove the *belly buttons* from a bowl of eggs I was preparing to scramble. He was a handy sort of friend who had an actual shop equipped with very sharp woodworking hobby tools. This friend also had a drinking hobby and, as a result of combining his two hobbies, the drinking and the woodworking, he had several fingers missing as well as one very short thumb. He promised that the next time he came over, he would have something for me to use in my frustrating efforts to separate the *belly button* from the egg yolk.

Several weeks later I invited him to a light southern breakfast of scrambled eggs, ham, red-eye gravy, biscuits, boiled peanuts, grits and Sierra Nevada Torpedo Ale, which is acknowledged throughout the land as the best cure for morning breath. When he arrived, he had a mysterious package wrapped up in recycled Christmas paper. He presented it with a great flourish of his short little thumb and a rolling of his one good eye. When the package was unwrapped, what did I discover but a very strange implement, which looked like a cross between a croupier's casino rake and a Mongolian yak fork. It was fashioned out of an exotic wood, pine I believe, and was designed solely for the efficient removal of the chicken egg's *belly button.* He said that this innovative new kitchen tool was a *Woogie Snatcher!* He mentioned that the exclamation point was an important part of the name. It worked just as advertised, and I urged him to take a patent out on the design. He observed that he didn't think enough people shared my weird *belly button obsession/phobia* to make mass production of the tool cost effective. I responded that he might be surprised at how many *belly button phobia* sufferers there were out there, and asked what might be my percentage if I was able to develop a market for this unique and necessary kitchen tool. He gave me a skeptical look but said, "What the hay, I'll make them and you sell them and we'll split the profits."

So! Good news for all you gentle readers out there in this great country of ours, and possibly in other English-reading countries. Let it be known that I have done some considerable research on the INTER-NET and have discovered that, in fact, the regular consumption of the chicken egg *belly button* might possibly be harmful to your personal human body. With this carefully researched and developed information at hand, it is strongly recommended that anyone reading this official *Junque Science Study* get in touch with my new company, *Woogie Snatchers R Us,* and we will send you your own personal snatcher for the mere price of $24.99 plus shipping of $14.99 for a grand total of $39.98 before taxes and a reasonable handling charge. These handy new items make fine gifts for the holiday season or Easter, when use of the chicken egg is especially common. For the next twenty-four hours only, the lucky buyer of six or more of these units will be presented with a leather-like cardboard holster which will provide a convenient means of wearing the *woogie snatcher* as an attractive belt accessory while working in the kitchen. Contact us today! Call Beachwood 45789 and ask for the *Woogie Snatcher INTER-NET Late Night Special Television Offer.* And remember, if you purchase six units, you will be sent a leather-like, cardboard belt-supported holster for your own personal use in the kitchen.

And speaking of kitchen matters, in addition to my very normal and reasonable *belly-button phobia,* I also have another bothersome issue with eggs. My other problem with the chicken egg is that I have a strong aversion to the white of the egg, which, unfortunately, seems to play a large role in the overall egg design. As a result of this phobic condition, I can only eat eggs that have been well scrambled, and even then, they have to be so very diligently beaten, with the whites and the yolks so completely blended, that no white is seen. And, of course, the *belly buttons* must be removed using my custom-designed *Woogie Snatcher!* (pat. pend.)

Through years of trial-and-error experimentation, I have discovered that the best way to blend the eggs, in preparation to making them properly scrambled, is to *beat them like a redheaded stepchild.* It can occasionally work to merely beat the chicken egg like a rented mule, but this secondary method is an inferior blending process and not nearly as satisfactory as the more effective redheaded stepchild method. If you are now, or ever have been, a redheaded stepchild, you know what I'm talking about.

Late breaking news! It can be now revealed that our Research and Development Laboratory is hard at work developing a design for our soon-to-be-released new product: the *Redheaded Stepchild Egg Beater!* Stepparents! This is how you can tame those wild redheaded and freckle-faced stepchildren that are making you crazy with their redheaded behavior. This new product will serve you well whether you are in the kitchen or out behind the woodshed. It beats both chicken eggs and boisterous children equally well and with similar success. You will want to invest in several as they can become damaged when used upon a squirmish child.

Introducing the New Digital High-Speed Wireless Message Device, Another Modern Miracle!

OVER THIS PAST WEEKEND MY TEENAGE DAUGHTER, Savannah A. Kilbourne, the finest daughter in all the land, and I have worked together to invent a novelty device for communicating with your fellow drivers, those persons also known as *flaming idiots!* This new device is now available on the open market and will provide comfort and a sense of well-being to owners as they motor down the highways and byways of life at speeds higher than are generally allowed by law. This device is wireless and considerably less expensive to purchase than your average cell phone. It is also far more personal and much easier to operate. Also, you need not sign a two-year contract to get one; and unlike the cell phone, it's not illegal to operate while driving … yet.

This new digitally operated high-speed wireless communication device is a basic hand-operated ping pong paddle sort of thingie with a series of very attractive holes drilled through the laminated wood along the top rim. These neatly drilled holes are then threaded with a sort of spiral coiled strand of plastic wire to be used to attach various appropriate and important messages that you might wish to convey to your fellow motorist in the next lane. The message pages are shiny white plastic with convenient tabs on the bottoms for ease of use. They are the size and shape of the circular section of the paddle. It doesn't require batteries and has no *on-off* switch. All in all, it is a very neat and modern package.

Provided with the device will be a variety of messages with which to address almost any sort of situation that might arise between neighboring motorists, traveling side by side at high speeds. Of course, there are possible safety issues that need to be addressed, such as the fact that often you have to press your knees against the bottom of the steering wheel in order to maintain some minimal degree of control over your speeding automobile while you sort through the numerous message choices. While doing the knee steering and message selection, you are encouraged to smile engagingly at the driver in the neighboring car as if to say, "Hold on, I've got a message for you so please be patient and try to remain a safe distance from my car as I'm steering with my knees."

When choosing which message to use, it is important to sort through your various emotions at play in the situation. For example, do you find that you are experiencing love at first sight with the driver in the next lane, or do you want to see that person burn in hell forever after they have just viciously cut you off? If the answer is the latter, you choose the following message: *You are going to hell with gasoline soaked drawers on for that last stupid move, you flaming idiot!*

However, if love is in the air, you have several actions to consider. The more traditional, old-fashioned action that a person might employ, prior to the invention of the New Digital High-Speed Wireless Message Device, A Modern Miracle, when gently trying to get the attention of a new love object who is ignoring you, would have been to employ a "high speed intervention" (HSI), by affectionately brushing your car up against his/her car in such a way as to be able to gently force him/her off the road so that you can exchange vital contact information, including insurance companies.

The main drawback to this more old-fashioned approach is that occasionally you might inadvertently guide the object of your desire's automobile into a large piece of slow-moving farm machinery; or worse, perhaps the target of your desire will be lovingly nudged into a bridge abutment. Not so good for beginning a long-term relationship.

Not to worry! With our new high-technology communication invention, those dreary cares are a thing of the past. We are now in the age of the newly invented Digital High-Speed Wireless Message Device, A Modern Miracle! The safer, more humane answer to obtaining the attention of a new love object is to use the message paddle to convey your deepest longing. After avidly searching through your inventory of messages to convey your deepest feelings to this sweet and gentle creature in the next lane, you may choose from the following sentiments, filled with a deep longing, such as, *Pull over immediately, I think I love you!* Or the even more thoughtful message, indicating a clear desire for a deep future commitment, *Will you have my baby? Please pull over at the next rest stop!*

On the other hand, if romance isn't in the air at that particular moment, and you are more curious about where the neighboring driver might have earned his/her driver's license, you might shuffle through the message inventory, again, while attempting to keep you car within its designated lane with the use of dexterous knee pressure, and choose the following, *Where did you get your driver's license? From a box of Cracker Jacks? You flaming idiot!*

Unfortunately, we have all encountered one of those cars that have a burnt-out motor or thrown valve, or is just an obscene oil barge with a dark greasy fossil-based plume following behind for a mile or more. These drivers are rude and very inconsiderate of the quality of our environment and cause horrendous air pollution. What do we want to say to them to convey our displeasure at the environmental disaster they are causing? My suggestion would be the following. *Excuse me but I believe your car is on fire. I'll notify the Highway Patrol for you. You flaming idiot!* Another useful message that is often flashed to the driver of an automobile in wrecked and dilapidated condition is, *Excuse me, but I believe a part just fell off of your wreck. You flaming idiot!*

If you have just passed an individual whom you would very much like to get to know better, we provide appropriate and polite messages to help convey your feelings to this driver. On a more authoritative note would be the message, *Follow me home, or else!* while a much more gentle and non-threatening message would be, *Can I follow you home? I promise I'll try and behave.*

Unfortunately, we have all encountered the frustrating driver who is simply not paying attention. These people clutter up the roads and highways and make driving much more dangerous for the rest of us. There is always the dazed driver who has driven for the past twenty miles with his/her blinker on while he/she operates his/her automobile in a semi-conscious state. My advice is to put those knees to work on the steering wheel while you thumb through your message paddle for the perfect snappy comment, such as *Helllllloooo, Hellllloooo, Anyone home over there? You flaming idiot!* or you might select the thoughtful sentiment, *Turn your blinking blinker off or I'll ram you to starboard!*

Then there is the opposite flaming idiot who never seems to realize they even have specific warning lights to be used to indicate that a left or right turn is in their immediate future. We all have seen the *Visualize World Peace* bumper stickers on cars all over the country. With our new Digital High-Speed Wireless Message Device, a Modern Miracle! there will be a paddleboard message that exhorts, *Visualize using your turn signal, you flaming idiot!*

We have all had to avoid rear-ending the driver who refuses to turn his/her headlights on until it is pitch black outside. If it is the time of a full moon, sometimes they don't use their headlights at all! They must think they are conserving gas by not using their lights. Well, get out the old message paddle and let them know your true feelings. Get those knees engaged on the wheel and begin shopping for the perfect message, such as, *Headlights! Headlights! Turn on your headlights, you flaming idiot, or I'll ram you on the port side!*

And finally, some of us may have seen that driver who doesn't seem to be in full control of his vehicle. He weaves back and forth while making wild waving gestures at cars in the neighboring lanes. You wonder what is going on with him and why he is driving so erratically. The driver who comes to mind always seems to be driving a dark grey Land Rover that is only partially under control. There is the perfect paddle message for this driver, as follows. *What are you doing, steering with your knees? You flaming idiot!*

Note:

We are currently soliciting investment capital with which to begin mass-producing these devices so as to make them available to every member of the American motoring public. Your liability risk as a potential investor is not to be a concern as each unit will come with a clearly printed disclaimer emphasizing that the manufacturer, and it various agents, is/are not responsible for any harm that might come to the user through personal violence brought against them by the message recipient.

The manufacturer will also not be responsible for any failed relationships or unwanted pregnancies which might occur or have been initiated through the use of our new Digital High-Speed Wireless Message Device, a Modern Miracle! No guarantee is furnished or implied.

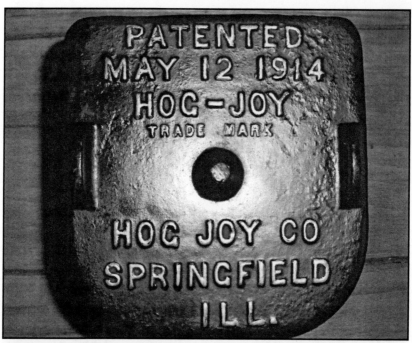

Behold the Hog-Powered Porkgasmic Belly Rotator, a modern miracle! It can be plainly seen that this pleasure-bringing device comes together in several basic pieces, each guaranteed for life. There is the sturdy cast iron frame, which includes the insecticide reservoir. Then there is your heavy cast iron barrel, which brings so much pleasure to beast, and man. And then there is your cast iron plunger thingie with all the pretty writing on it.

The Porkgasmic Belly Rotator

ONE OF THE MOST UNUSUAL ITEMS still remaining in my possession following my years of acquiring strange and unusual *collectibles,* also known to some of my friends as *junque,* is a cast iron barrel device that refers to itself as a *Hog Joy.* The antique dealer from whom I purchased this item said it was referred to as a *Missouri Hog Joy* in the antique trade.

The affable owner of the antique barn, up in Amador City, explained that this was the only Hog Joy he had ever seen. He guessed that there wouldn't be more than a half-dozen in the whole state of California, although they would be more common in the Midwest, where they were used back in the 1920s and 1930s. He explained that the device was employed by hog farmers to control bug infestations on the underside of their swine.

The all cast iron device was appealing in its simplicity. The design was based upon a barrel-shaped roller, a reservoir, a plunger, and a tray underneath the roller. The reservoir was filled with a sticky insecticide and then the plunger was inserted into it. The heavy plunger forced the insecticide through the reservoir and into a tray beneath the barrel. The barrel rolled forward with the momentum of the hog, as the animal was strongly encouraged to belly over it. It was hog powered! As the barrel rolled, it became coated with the insecticide in the tray, which was then transferred to the hog's belly where the pests especially liked to congregate.

The hog wasn't given any choice in the matter as the Hog Joy was bolted to the floor of a narrow wooden chute that the animals were caused to pass through, in line, one at a time. The hog was not inconvenienced in any way by being subjected to this mandatory procedure, and in fact, it soon became apparent to the hogs that this was a thoroughly enjoyable process that they might wish to repeat, more times than the farmer had patience for.

After I got my very own Hog Joy home, I took the cast iron plunger thingie out of the reservoir, and in doing this, discovered a very informative pamphlet that had been underneath the plunger dealie since before the dawn of time. While the pamphlet was in near-perfect condition, you could tell from the typestyle, the yellowed parchment and especially from the wording, that it was really old.

Note to the reader: I have faithfully translated this ancient document as carefully as possible. This encouraging information was provided to the prospective buyer, as follows:

Announcing the Now Available and Newly Offered Hog Joy!

We are presenting another modern miracle from the Hog Joy Co. of Springfield, Ill. This exciting new product is popularly known by its full name, "The Porkgasmic Belly Rotator and Pest Eradicator, A Hog's Joy!" Our corporate motto remains, "Happy hogs make sweet pork!" We assure you this modern farming device brings joy to all hogs subjected to its use.

Hog farmers from throughout the American Midwest are extolling the virtues of this newly available piece of farm equipment as a means of ridding their swine of the bristle ouchies and the bung snouts, both pests that plague and aggravate your fully grown, yet sensitive, meat hog. The Hog Joy is currently enjoying heavy use by your Midwestern hog farmers as a means of controlling these troublesome pest infestations on the delicate underside of their prize swine. This modern device offers an effective means of controlling the snouts and ouchies while also providing their hogs with a bit of final pleasure as they go happily on their way to the packing house.

It will be of interest to know that this device is portable and easily moved from hog yard to hog yard. It can be shared among neighboring hoggers, if that arrangement is so desired. The modern equipment is designed around a heavyweight iron roller, which becomes covered with the scientifically developed insecticide provided to the buyer, which then coats the tender underbelly bacon of your meat hog for all the important purposes stated above.

By intelligent design, this new device features a heavy cast iron gravity feed plunger, which evacuates a reservoir built cleverly on the side of the roller unit. The insecticide is then served to a dished gutter underneath the Hog Joy, where it becomes available to coat the roller as it rotates with each hog's passing. There is little for the farmer to do but watch his hogs grunt and squeal in pleasure as the especially formulated insecticide coats their nethers, from hock to ham.

Following extensive modern research, it has been learned that, if there be any possible negative aspect of the new Hog Joy, it is that the device brings too much pleasure to your hog, so that, being the intelligent creatures that they are, after experiencing their initial belly roll across the pleasure-bringing sturdy cast iron drum, with your lifetime guarantee, they attempt to back up and have another go at her. If they are blocked from backing over the roller again by their fellow hogs, as eager as they are, they will circle around and queue up once more, in line for another pass, even after they have already fully benefited from an initial treatment. These are joyful hogs!

It has been known to happen that your hog farmer, with an average herd of five hundred swine, may record the passing through of several thousands of the beasts before the treatment work is completed. "How can this be?" the bemused hogger rightfully asks. Well, Sir, the answer is that many, if not all, of your hogs are getting back in line to have another go down the chute, thus treating themselves to additional pleasurable trips over the Hog Joy.

The sensation of rolling across the Hog Joy while having their infested bellies coated with this cool and soothing balm, gives the hogs such intense pleasure that many farmers describe the device as being orgasmic for their porcine livestock. Hence the clever name, "Porkgasmic Belly Rotator and Pest Eradicator," has been adopted and accepted by the U.S. Patents Office. Again, our motto is, "Happy hogs make sweet pork!"

We mention with some hesitancy that, if truth were told, there is a colorful story going around these days, which we here at Hog Joy, Inc. of Springfield, Ill. cannot verify, nor can we genuinely disprove. The story at issue is that one farmer recently discovered with concern, in the late hours, well after vespers, that his wife was missing from their marriage bed.

After searching throughout the house, he was finally able to locate her out in the hog yard seated astride his proud new Hog Joy. She was easily located once he entered within hearing distance as she had set up such a noisy grunting and squealing while exercising his Hog Joy, that she had the chickens awake and the rooster crowing. It is told that she had that Hog Joy hotter than a snake's belly in a wagon rut.

Well, Sir, you can imagine that she was not infested with any belly pests, such as the bristle ouchies or the bung snouts, nor was she troubled with any "womanly frustrations" once she finished her effort on that Missouri Hog Joy! No Sir! It is said, that Mr. Hog Farmer, no name is necessary here, experienced some difficulty getting his wife off of, and away from, the device and back inside the house. Of possible interest is the fact that later that same week, he discovered that the Hog Joy had been relocated into the spare bedroom of the main house. We again say that we cannot verify these rumors and only relay them to you as we feel it is our responsibility to offer a word of caution.

As of the printing of this advertisement, the newly patented Hog Joy is available at your local farm equipment dealer for a price that

*is fair and reasonable. Consider the comfort and happiness of your
hogs, as well as the missus, when making your decision to purchase."*

Well Sir! You can rest assured that I don't plan to let my lady
friends anywhere near my Missouri Hog Joy unless they are properly
chaperoned as I keep it securely locked up in my spare bedroom,
much the same as the Hog Farmer's missus does. In any case, I'm
pretty sure none of my lady friends are plagued by the bung snouts
or the bristle ouchies.

Observe nicotine-crazed smokers unable to wait until they get to shore before "lighting up" to enjoy that crisp freshness provided by large volumes of tars and nicotine, as well as trace amounts of benzene and hydrochlorides. It's Springtime For Your Lungs! I always smoke while I'm swimming, or just in the bathtub or shower, as this prevents the cigarette from burning too fast.

The Discovery of the Exclamation Point!

I WAS UP IN THE ATTIC LAST WEEKEND, hiding from my daughter, who wanted help with her Geometry homework. While up there I came across a box that was being held down by several other larger boxes. After I dug my way down to it, much like a paleontologist digging in Mesopotamia, I discovered that it was full of old *Life* magazines, circa 1960, which is approximately one-half century ago. These magazines were in the larger 10"x 14" format made popular by *Life, The Saturday Evening Post,* and *Colliers,* among others.

I spent several hours going through a dozen or so, and was amazed and delighted to discover that the use of electricity within the home was apparently sponsored in or around 1960 by a company called General Electric.

I came to this updated understanding about the discovery of new and exciting uses for electricity from studying the tremendous amount of advertising in each one of these issues of *Life*. As my teenage daughter Savannah stated, "It looks like these magazines are pretty much all advertising." She then asked how it might be possible that doctors could strongly recommend the use of cigarettes as *health aids and stress reducers*. I mentioned that my doctor used to smoke while he was giving me my annual physical exam. This was back in the 1960s as well.

The reader of this essay will quickly see that advertisers also used an amazing amount of exclamation points while advertising in 1960!!! In fact, I believe this might have been the year that the exclamation point was discovered by that same company calling itself General Electric. As a side note, I had a good friend once tell me that excessive use of the exclamation point was like being forced to watch someone else's kid jump up and down!!!

General Electric's marketing department apparently felt there was something about watching kids jump up and down that would sell electrical products, as demonstrated by the following advertisement. *No home should be without the brand new GE Electric Clock! The user merely plugs this device right into a wall in their home and electricity comes into the clock and causes it to run, and run, and run! No winding necessary, ever again! This new time keeping marvel is silent and accurate! Have one for every room where there is electricity!* If it's cloudy out and your sundial isn't keeping good time, the new all-weather electric clock is your answer! Amazing! I suppose an inconvenient power outage would greatly affect the accuracy of a new electric clock, but this was not brought to the buying public's attention!

The wise homeowner could also purchase an *Electronic Dishwasher* from this same company whose slogan was *Progress Is Our Most Important Product!* The *Brand New!* electronic dishwasher was named the *New GE Mobile Maid* and had wheels, which allowed *Mrs. Modern Homemaker* to wheel it into any room of the house that had a wall socket, which provided electricity necessary to make it operate properly. The owner could make it work without the benefit of electricity, but the product devolved into a basic washbasin in that case. Not that it wouldn't still be more useful than taking your dirty crockery down to the creek to wash.

I believe one of the most compelling aspects of the Brand New GE Mobile Maid Dishwasher, with *Power Shower!* was the fact that it could be used in any room that had a faucet, which was needed to provide water to the machine. Imagine doing last night's dinner dishes in your bathroom while you are showering or brushing your dentures. *Progress Is Our Most Important Product* yet again!

In the category of home laundry needs, General Electric offered a brand new *Flameless Clothes Dryer!* that was operated by electricity and gave Mrs. Modern Homemaker *A feeling of confidence in the ability of the new flameless clothes dryer to handle even the most delicate fabrics with safety, without being destroyed by fire!*

The homeowner of the early 60s could also opt for a home with "electric house heating" rather that the previously popular wood house heating, or coal house heating, or even steam house heating. The advertising line was, *Electric house heating is here now! Better Living Electrically!*

The wise and modern consumer could also purchase a Portable Electric Hand Mixer, that *beats, whips and mixes drinks!* On a more personal note, this product description sounds very much like an old gal I used to go out with!!

One of my favorite new electric devices, which made the home-maker's life so much more convenient and pleasurable, through living better electrically, was the invention of the electric icemaker. *Electric Ice Maker built right into your freezer compartment! IceMagic replaces every cube you use, automatically, cube after cube after cube! Frost never forms! No trays to fill, spill, or pry loose! You'll want an IceMagic for your kitchen today!*

And then there was the all new GE Electric Can Opener: *Opens cans at a touch of a finger, smoothly, cleanly, no jagged edges!* This item came with an automatic electric knife sharpener, which was offered as an accessory!

Although I did not see it advertised in my *Life* magazine, I suspect GE was equally enthusiastic about their Nuclear Reactor design that may have contributed to the Fukushima nuclear disaster in 2011. I could have written the ad: *Introducing the all new GE Nuclear Reactor. Energy for the future!! Safe and effective!! Lots of power in this big baby, yet afford-able for most American and foreign communities!!*

Further on in the six-decades-old *Life* magazines were numerous other recently developed *conveniences,* designed and developed to make Mr. and Mrs. American Homemaker's life easier and more pleasant, including the following products:

The *Brand new Schick Electric Razor!* This product was offered with three speeds that gave a closer, faster, and smoother shave. *No more razor blades to hone!*

The newest innovation in the automotive industry: Auto Air! Cool air by the carload! No more steamy, sweltering road trips with a hot Granny complaining about the heat!

The modern new innovation in food preservation and presentation. Glass! Glass containers show you exactly what you are buying. What's left over stores safely and stays fresh, in the original glass container, because there's nothing in glass to change the original flavor, and there's nothing to hide!

Further on in the magazine, my eye was caught by a full-page spread promoting the *New Loveable Bra* produced by the Loveable Brassiere and Girdle Company of New Haven, Connecticut. The bra appeared to consist mainly of a pair of sharply pointed cones of heavy white cotton that boasted *spiral stitched cups!!* These cups provided something referred to as *dualift* that was a great benefit to the *modern woman* of the day and were also capable of ending *uncomfortable curl up.* (In the name of propriety, let's not ask what *uncomfortable curl up* means.) The price was a reasonable $1.50 each. The color selection was white, white, or white. Obviously the Loveable Brassiere and Girdle Company of New Haven, Connecticut also realized the commercial benefit of using the exclamation point!

Then there was the all-new electric typing machine. *For the professional secretary working in a business office, the new Royal Electric Typewriter is what she has been waiting for!* No more *pounding the keys* with this modern device! *It takes electricity and makes it do more for the typist!* It could etch, position, and ink all in one smooth operation. *Plug it into any common wall socket!*

As mentioned above, the marketing of cigarettes as a health aid was rampant in the year 1960. This epidemic of cigarette promotion was partially led by the Old Gold brand with their *New Old Gold*

Spin Filter, which spins and cools the smoke to a pleasant 78 degrees!" It went on to state that *The cooler the smoke, the better the taste!* The ad emphasized that seventy-eight degrees Fahrenheit was cooler than the normal body temperature of the smoker. Although the ad didn't emphasize this fact, I have to assume that your more serious smokers could look forward to much lower than normal body temperatures as the years of heavy smoking take their final toll.

While the Old Gold brand might have the benefits of the new *spin filter,* the Salem cigarette brand promoted the healthful benefits of their newest cigarette innovation–*high porosity paper*–with great enthusiasm. *The new Salem Cigarette air softens each puff with our special new High Porosity paper which breathes new mildness into the smoke and new freshness into the flavor!* Apparently this exceptional innovation caused the nicotine and tar-laden smoke to be very similar to Mother Nature's own fresh outside air. *The new High Porosity paper blends fresh air into the smoke! When you take a puff, it's springtime!* Smoking Salems must be especially rewarding in the dead of winter when you long for the coming of warm sunny days. Wow! A bit of High Porosity paper combined with a good deep drag of tar and nicotine and hark! It's springtime for your lungs!

PART EIGHT

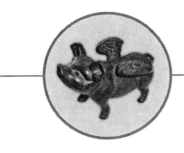

OTHER STORIES OF
GREAT INTEREST

Marcel the French Bulldog is seen wearing his Temperature Modification Cloth. He had a faulty thermostat, much like the Deluxe Oldsmobile, and easily would become overheated if not kept cool and moist. Reilley kept a wet bit of toweling on Marcel's head to protect him from the rays of the sun, much the same as a convertible top would have done had there been one.

Carolina to California in Thirty-Six Hours, Guaranteed or Your Money Back

IWAS A FULL-TIME COLLEGE STUDENT searching the *Riders Wanted* bulletin board in an effort to figure how my roommate, Johnny Hatcher, and I were going to get to California for our summer jobs. Neither of us owned a car. We were sophomores majoring in Forestry at Clemson University, in beautiful South Carolina, and had both been hired to work on the Forestry Crew at Lassen Volcanic National Park, which was somewhere in Northern California.

Only one *Riders Wanted* ad looked promising. It read, *Take a ride in a luxury Oldsmobile topless convertible car. South Carolina to California in 36 hours, guaranteed or your money back.* The wording seemed somehow redundant since it is generally understood that, by design, a convertible is a topless car. The ad was soliciting two riders to share in the cost of gas and went on to state that $50 would be required in advance to reserve a seat. The *cross country adventure* would begin the following Saturday at 6:00 A.M., *Rain or Shine. Contact Reilley James.*

The ad further described the car as a *fine* Oldsmobile convertible. Potential riders were cautioned to pack light, as the trunk would be mostly filled with *extra tires for the trip.* Extra tires for the trip? This comment alone should have waved a big red flag, but the glamour of riding across the country in a fine Oldsmobile convertible overcame attention to cautionary clues. We signed on and paid up.

The following Saturday we arrived to find Reilley busily changing a flat tire. The *deluxe* Oldsmobile appeared to have seen some very hard miles and rough handling. One headlight was missing, and Reilley explained that his French bulldog, Marcel, had recently eaten much of the front passenger seat. The seat had originally been a bench seat, but Marcel had made it into a roughly modified set of bucket seats with his incessant craving for whatever nutrients might be found in leather upholstery. Reilley commented that Marcel was most likely suffering from a leather deficiency of some sort. He further mentioned that eating all that leather had given Marcel a little gas.

He also commented that he was installing the best of all the tires, but the extra spares would be needed because the retread tires tend to come apart at high speeds. He further explained that we would have to average 75 to 80 mph in order to make his ETA of crossing the border at Needles, California, in thirty-six hours. I had just finished an *Introduction to Logic* course, taught by the well-known author, Dr. Richard Parker, the previous week; and my newly acquired deductive reasoning skills told me that, based on Reilley's statement, 1) tires come apart at high speeds, and 2) we would be driving all the way across the country at high speeds; therefore, ergo, we were guaranteed some considerable tire troubles on this trip. I was deeply concerned. However, my concerns were not addressed.

The previous Carolina to California land speed record had been set by another Clemson student, one Tommy Thompson, driving his brand new two-door hardtop convertible Pontiac Ventura. Thompson had made the trip in thirty-eight hours and change. Reilley was determined to beat Thompson's record. He felt strongly that Oldsmobiles were faster than Pontiacs. Our responsibility was to bear witness to that fact.

As we were loading up, I called out "shotgun," which placed me in what remained of the front passenger seat with the excessively flatulent Marcel for the first day. The four of us, Reilley, Johnny, myself, and Marcel, were all in a good mood and looking forward to starting the road adventure. We shook hands, and paws, all around. Then after Marcel gave a flatulent toot of goodbye, we *lit out for the territories.* Johnny was in the back buried among the luggage and supplies needed by three persons and one dog planning on being gone from home for three months. The trunk was full of spare tires and beer. We soon discovered that putting the beer in the trunk was not good planning. Johnny offered to ride in the trunk with the beer.

Somewhere near Memphis, Tennessee, I suggested that it was time for lunch and said I would be willing to take a turn at driving. Reilley demurred. Since we still had gas in the tank, he didn't want to stop. We would eat while continuing in a forward direction at a high rate of speed. My sainted mother had prepared the food for Johnny and me with the understanding that Johnny's mother would provide the drinks. Mrs. Hatcher had given Johnny $20 and told him to buy whatever we wanted to drink on the trip. I'm sure she had some sort of sodas or healthful juices in mind. However, being typical young college boys, we opted for two cases of Carling Black Label at $10 per case. It was well known that Carling's unofficial marketing theme was *Carling Black Label. We rent it to you. You only have it temporarily.* This warning did not deter us, and by the time we had arrived in California, the Carling was all gone, having been given back on the shoulders of the highways and byways of eight states.

It had proven difficult to get Reilley to stop in order to download some of the beers Johnny and I had been drinking. We had just recently passed a very attractive sign somewhere in Tennessee that proclaimed the magic words, "Rest Stop Ahead." When I enthusiastically pointed it out to Reilley, his response was, "I'll slow down when we go by the sign, if you want."

Somewhere in the middle of Arkansas, our upbeat mood was beginning to deteriorate. After driving hard for over twelve hours, we were windblown and sunburned. Then it began to rain, very large cold drops. We strongly urged, actually demanded, that Reilley stop and put up the top. He finally pulled over and ceremoniously pushed the button that operated the power top. After much groaning and squeaking of distressed metal, a bare framework slowly arose to show a few charred pieces of fabric, none larger than a dinner napkin. With a sense of dread, we realized the meaning of his curious description of a *topless* convertible.

Reilley casually mentioned that there had been a small fire and the top had burned off during a recent high-speed *event* involving the incautious use of some 151-proof rum and Cuban cigars. No further details were forthcoming. He then pushed the button again to retract the bare frame. Reilley mentioned that he thought the frame *detracted from the appearance of the car* when it was in the up position.

We finally found an overpass and stopped until the worst of the rain had passed. Reilley encouragingly mentioned that we had made over seven hundred miles so far and had only a couple thousand more to go. Marcel had busily chewed the seat down to the springs by this time and was suffering from considerable gastric activity. We could use the fresh air that was provided by the topless convertible.

After what seemed like days later, just outside of Oklahoma City, I mentioned to Reilley that I noticed he had a radio installed in the dash of his *fine Oldsmobile convertible car*. I knew that the famous DJ, Wolfman Jack, operated a rock and roll station in this region. It might be worth tuning in to relieve the endless howling of the wind as we drove through the night. He agreed that, yes, there was a radio that came with the car. Unfortunately, it had somehow been disabled in the same fire that had consumed the car's top. He went on to say, however, that the eight-track tape player seemed to work fine if we wanted some music. When Johnny asked what kind of tapes he had on board, Reilley replied that, actually, Marcel had eaten all the tapes but one, which was the *Creedence Clearwater Revival* album. Apparently Marcel was not a fan of bayou rock. At the end of the trip, it was conservatively estimated by Johnny, who had a way with numbers, that we had listened to this album over one hundred times. I never want to hear *Susie Q, Lookin' Out My Back Door, Proud Mary,* or *Sweet Hitch-Hiker* again in this lifetime!

The previously described events continued apace. After two days and one long night, we entered California at the little desert town of Needles, in 34 hours and some few minutes. I recall this was just before vespers on Sunday evening. As we drove through Needles, we were rolling on only one of the original tires, having shed retreads at high speeds in Texas, New Mexico, and Arizona. Marcel was proudly driving with his little paws on the steering wheel while sitting on Reilley's lap. No refunds were made.

The Swashbuckling Adventures of
Horatio Hornblower
And
The Womanizing Cad, Harry Flashman

MY GOOD FRIEND and boon Friday Afternoon Gentlemen's
Billiards Society companion, Richard Parker, has been a devotee of
George MacDonald Fraser's *Flashman* Series for many years. The
setting for these stories is described as "Voluptuous Victorian Eng-
land." I have a copy given to me by Richard on the occasion of my
birthday back in the late Philistine Era, circa 1989 to be precise.

The book is imaginatively titled, *Flashman and the Damsel in
Distress* or *Flashman to the Rescue* or something similarly swashbuckling. The story is described as follows:

> *Harry Flashman wenches his way to glory as a scoundrel of the first
> water. Flashman is a cheat, a bully, an infamous womanizer and
> a cad. He is a lecher, a rotten bounder and a big coward who hides
> behind women's skirts as he attempts to get within them. Harry
> Flashman does not always act like a perfect gentleman.*

Sounds like my kind of guy, wenching his way to glory through
three hundred steaming pages of swashbuckling and womanizing.
Also sounds a little like my boon companion, one Richard Parker.
Do I detect an alter ego at play here?

On the other hand, my elder brother, Dixon Roy "Dickie" Kilbourne, a Great American and Christian Gentleman, who is my
favorite, best, and only brother, does not concern himself with
naughty reading such as my less sanctified good friend Richard
Parker. Dickie's idea of a great afternoon is to be left alone among
his endless stacks of very old *National Geographic* magazines. These

magazines are so old and outdated that the most recent copy was on the newsstands during the Eisenhower Administration. The first term.

When my best brother is not perusing dusty old *National Geographics,* looking for *anthropological* photos of topless Samoan natives, to proselytize to no doubt, he will be found deeply immersed in one of the titles in the endless *Horatio Hornblower* series by C. S. Forester. He has read the entire series numerous times. If this favored brother is allowed to come back through the benefits of reincarnation, I am sure he will arrive in the person of the good Captain Hornblower, since he knows more about this fictional hero of the world's oceans that anyone alive. Apparently, similar to Harry Flashman, Horatio Hornblower is the alter ego of many men of a certain age. My brother is of a certain age.

The titles found in Hornblower's adventures on the briny deep are predictable and deeply boring. Examples of the sort of unimaginative wording the titles being discussed suffer from are approximately as follows: *Captain Hornblower Sails the Bounding Main, Commodore Hornblower* (he got a raise!) *Commands Her Majesty's Royal Navy,* and the all-time exciting mind-blower, *Admiral Hornblower Sails His Big Ship upon the Ocean.*

I have a much better idea of what these stodgy old titles require to bring new, younger, and possibly more hip readers into the Hornblower Fan Club. My suggestions include, in this order, as he continues to enjoy promotions in rank: *Lieutenant Hornblower Meets the Pirates of the Caribbean in 3-D, Captain Hornblower Discovers an Island Populated by Naked Samoan Natives, Commodore Hornblower Rescues Damsels in Distress from Harry Flashman, The Womanizing Cad,* and possibly to wind up the series, once and for all, *Admiral Hornblower Visits Davey Jones' Locker.*

Authors and Titles Not on
The New York Times Best-Seller List

HEREIN BEGINS A BRIEF AND WHIMSICAL discussion of two obscure, but highly recommendable titles that I've enjoyed multiple times over the years. These titles include *The Magic Christian* by Terry Southern, and the winner of the all-time most unusual book award, *Adventures in Oatmeal* by George Vermont, which was published in 1952. Vermont's book was introduced to me by my previous, first, ex, and only wife, Nancy Lynne Quiggle, *Girl Scout Counselor in Charge*, not long after we had crossed paths while hiking up in the deep woods of Lassen Volcanic Park, in Tehama County in Northern California.

The Vermont book is a queer little adventure story of sorts, featuring high school chums Karl Kleenkutt and the Hayseed Brothers (*known to their friends as Jim and Bill*), as well as the chronic juvenile delinquent, Needles Grogan. In retrospect, I believe at their age I was more like the ill-behaved Needles Grogan while my elder brother, Dixon Roy Kilbourne, a Christian Gentleman, was much more like Karl Kleenkutt and his friends. *Adventures in Oatmeal* may qualify as the all-time most unusual book I have read in my several decades of reading. To verify that statement, I offer the first paragraph directly from the book. Thanks to George Vermont, wherever he may be.

Karl Kleenkutt leaped from his bed with a smile as the first rays of the morning sun found their way into his open windows. As was his daily custom, he greeted the day with fifty push-ups and sixty-five deep knee bends. He then rushed to the bathroom, washed himself with a generous amount of soap and hot water, and brushed his teeth vigorously, being very careful to massage his gums and to brush the inside of his teeth with as much vigor as he had used on the outside. Returning to his room, he slipped into his moleskin trousers, which he had chosen for their serviceability and smart good looks, as well as a clean white t-shirt. A pair of stout cushion sole heavy brogans with built-in arch supporters completed his attire. Karl's mother handed him a bowl of steaming hot oatmeal as he hurried into the kitchen. He took the bowl and bade his mother a cheery good morning. Mrs. Kleenkutt, holding back a look of great pride, asked Karl if he wanted his usual two quarts of milk. "No Mother," replied Karl. "Now that we're engaged in vigorous and healthful football practice, I believe that I'll need three quarts. Coach Paunchley says that milk builds strong bodies."

This bizarre little story soon gets even more exciting as Karl and his school chums, the Hayseed Brothers, stumble clumsily through late adolescence while attempting to avoid any sinful temptations that might defile their healthy young bodies. Fortunately, they were rarely successful. Their idea of a good time involves hiking all weekend while taking turns reciting passages from *The Boy Scout Manual.* These painfully sincere young high school chums were very different from Nancy Lynne Quiggle, *Girl Scout Counselor in Charge,* and her unorthodox approach to the great American institution of scouting. But that's another story.

The Magic Christian by Terry Southern, published in 1959, is an unforgettable little novel best described as being *wildly irreverent satire involving the study of human nature as it concerns the belief that bigger is better and whoever dies with the most toys wins.* The main character, Guy Grand, *a grand guy* as he likes to describe himself, is an eccentric billionaire with a deeply twisted sense of mischief. He is the ultimate prankster and has a great appreciation for complicated, and expensive, practical jokes.

In the title story of this collection of outrageous *situations* created by Guy Grand, *The S. S. Magic Christian* is the name of a retired luxury liner that Guy Grand buys, renovates, and markets as follows: "Each cabin on the Christian is a palace in miniature with appointments so lavish and so exquisite that they are better imagined than described." As planned, every possible thing goes wrong as the luxury voyage gets underway and Grand has his sick and twisted way with his captive group of passengers. His intention is to carry out various maniacal social experiments upon them once they are well out to sea and unable to escape his control.

During the extensive refitting, Guy Grand has had every stateroom on the luxury liner equipped with wall-sized television monitors, which cannot be turned off. There are no controls and the sets cannot be unplugged. They are on all day and night, without relief. This is how Grand perpetuates his mischief upon the innocent passengers. One memorable scene that occurs early in the voyage takes place on the ocean liner's bridge. The action that is, of course, televised and broadcast into every stateroom, shows the charismatic Captain of the *S.S. Magic Christian* being viciously attacked from behind by a rampaging gorilla.

The overpowered Captain is then shown being thrown overboard. At this point the screen of every television suddenly goes blank with static. The innocent passengers are left to their out-of-control imaginations at this point. Nothing is forthcoming for the rest of the night as the panicked passengers gather in the passageways and public areas to frantically discuss the emergency. The next morning sees the Captain strolling casually about the decks while greeting the passengers in his everyday charismatic way. This is merely one of many such outrageous mischiefs that Guy Grand inflicts upon the *Magic Christian's* unwary, and at this point, unwilling passengers.

In all of his bizarre situations, Guy Grand enjoys *making it hot for folks* by encouraging them to behave in ways they would never consider were it not for the vast amount of cash they are offered to participate in his outrageous mischief. He usually concludes one of his wicked pranks by commenting, "No real harm done surely," as he pays off various authorities for damages that occurred during the stunt. *It cost him a pretty penny to keep clear in the end* is often the last line in a chapter describing his effort to avoid legal complications after another bit of manic mischief is inflicted upon greedy, but naive members of the American public.

If I personally had full access to Guy Grand's bank account I would perpetrate a grand hoax on the infamous Raider Nation. This group of extreme fans of the Oakland Raiders football team hold their violent and unscrupulous players in such high regard that the status given to the most brutal and testosterone-soaked individuals is almost god-like. The fans that occupy the Raider Nation *black hole* in the end zone dress up with such outrageous outfits and makeup that it appears the actual game is secondary. This grand prank would be dedicated to all those rank members of the Raider Nation. I would make it hot for them.

It would go down like this. The much feared Raiders team would take the field attired in classic ballerina costumes complete with frilly pink codpieces, tap shoes, and angel wings. These brutes would all be heavily made up with lipstick, mascara, and very low fashion wigs. They would commence to dance around their amazed opponents with mincing steps while lightly bitch-slapping them and rolling their eyes with excitement. They would then prance down to the end zone where the Black Hole is located and gaily *double-lady-wave* (both hands up and fingers coyly wiggled) to the Raider Nation while shrieking with excitement. They would jump up and down as if they were in extreme bladder pain.

The stalwart Raider Nation would never fully recover from the mortification and dishonor visited upon them by their beloved Raiders. While the most faithful members of the black hole gang might begin to dress up in pink ballerina outfits with little Mary Jane strapped shoes, my guess is that a majority of the others would decide to stay at home where they can groom their pit bulls and tune up their low riders.

In response to the new all-time low in attendance and fan support, the current Oakland Coliseum would be converted into a children's ice hockey rink and the Raiders would begin playing all their home games at the Oakland High School stadium, where they would be allowed to play the high school team for practice.

This prank would cost a pretty penny to carry out, as each Raider-brute involved would have to be generously reimbursed to the tune of millions of dollars. No real harm done surely.

Come One – Come All!
A Worthwhile Seminar On Constipation, Diarrhea and Excessive Bodily Winds!

Absolutely Free and Without Charge!

This worthwhile one-hour seminar will be held on Thursday the
14th of July at 3:00 sharp.
Don't be late as seating is limited!
Dr. Bob's Intestinal Flatulence Clinic
210 Esplanade, Room 407

This is an excellent opportunity to invest one brief hour
of your valuable time in order to achieve
greater intestinal harmony!

This important information will be presented in
a knowledgeable and highly entertaining manner.

Slides, charts and graphs will be shown and discussed.
Questions are encouraged!
Light refreshments will be served at the end
of the presentation. Bring your friends!

The spacious and comfortable private conference room
is both air-conditioned and climate controlled!
Call Beachwood 45789 for further details.

Advertisement in local newspaper which caused this reporter to attend worthwhile Body Winds Seminar.

At the Flatulence and Constipation Seminar
With Dr. Bob and the Former Ms. Shrew

THIS RECENT SEMINAR I attended in beautiful downtown Savannah, Georgia, was missing only two things: dogs and ponies. Otherwise, it was a thoroughly entertaining sixty minutes of miscues and malfunctions. It could even be considered a *hot* show, as nearly two dozen of us were shoehorned into a smallish room where the inside temperature was quickly exceeding the outside temperature, and it was a warm afternoon out there.

While the seminar was promoted in the local daily as being a very valuable use of our time, it was actually a one-hour unrehearsed sales pitch. Furthermore, this blatant infomercial was inflicted upon us *seminarees* in a stuffy, overheated office that offered no possibility of escape. Claustrophobia was running rampant through the group within the first five minutes. There was one poor attendee who kept her eyes tightly clenched throughout the entire seminar as she gently rocked back and forth moaning softly to herself. *She was not in her happy place.*

The office was identified on the front door to be a Digestive and Intestinal Wind Clinic. The Principal, whom I will refer to as Dr. Robt. Milquetoste, since I could never pronounce his name, was actually a chiropractor, and looked very similar to Professor Snape in the Harry Potter movies. He was present and prepared to enlighten us on the main cause of chronic flatulence. The presentation was promoted in the local paper as a *Seminar on Body Wind.* His wife slash office manager was on hand to see that things went smoothly and that Dr. Bob didn't screw it up. Ms. Milquetoste and the good doctor were a matched set as she looked eerily like I would imagine Professor Snape's mother, who was not seen in the Harry Potter movies.

It must have required a substantial suspension of logic on their part for the Milquetostes to closely tie chronic flatulence into their own specialized field of chiropractics, but this couple was determined to explore a possible new market. Apparently, their traditional business was bogging down and they hoped to make inroads into a new clientele by targeting the many flatulence sufferers in their community.

As the seminar began, the wife/office manager member of the team strode up to the podium in a very officious manner. I was seated in the front row center of this crowded little room where I could have reached out, without stretching, and patted her on the head if the notion had occurred to me. It did not. I learned as time went by that if I did, I probably would have *pulled back a stump*, as they are wont to say in the Deep South.

In the first few minutes, I realized we were in for a longish session even though it had been marketed to the unsuspecting community as *one brief but extremely worthwhile hour out of your busy lives.*

So, here we are. The wife/office manager proudly, and with great determination, introduces her husband as simply *Dr. Bob* since his actual last name is such a convolution of vowels and consonants as to be almost too difficult to sound out. She explained that all their *hundreds* of patients referred to her husband as *Dr. Bob* rather than attempt to correctly pronounce his Middle-Eastern Jewish Armenian surname. She continued on, gently chuckling to herself, to explain that when they were married she had chosen to keep her maiden name (which I distinctly remember as *Shrew*) rather than deal with his. It finally became apparent that her main role in this D&P show was to add an element of humor. However, her attempt at humor was so lame that I ultimately took on the responsibility of providing some entertainment to those poor souls trapped in the little seminar room.

What we had here was a husband and wife team that was embarrassingly uncoordinated and painfully unrehearsed. I couldn't figure out which one was the dog and which was the pony, although the former Ms. Shrew's role seemed to consist mainly of making a series of low-key humming sounds of approval whenever Dr. Bob made an especially lame comment. She was also in charge of asking excruciatingly obvious questions of her husband, which he was to promptly answer, or she would redirect the question to the group. If satisfactory responses didn't come quickly enough from either Dr. Bob or the group, she would provide the answer herself.

An example of one of her questions to Dr. Bob, which he fumbled badly, was, "And where do we feel our flatulence the most?" When Dr. Bob didn't answer immediately, she snapped, "Well, in the tummy, of course!" The good doctor looked ashamed that he wasn't quite sharp enough to solve such a complicated riddle.

Ms. Shrew also made an ongoing effort to get the group to wake up and become involved with the questions, "Well then, why are we here this evening?" When she received NO response after thirty seconds of heavy silence, she said sternly, "Well, we're here because we have body wind, isn't that correct?" Again, NO response was offered. To break the silence I spoke up and declared that I actually never had the body winds but was there for two friends out in California who were chronic sufferers but couldn't make the seminar. This comment broke her planned rhythm, and she gave forth with a mighty frown in my direction.

Just as she was beginning to re-establish her momentum, Dr. Bob interrupted to ask her if the air conditioning was turned on. She glared at him and said, "Of course it's on, Dr. Bob!" He then began to make this question into a larger discussion by asking her what temperature the thermostat was set at since it seemed to be getting quite hot in the room. She snapped that it wasn't hot at all but was VERY PLEASANT in the room. Unfortunately, Dr.

Bob persisted with his line of awkward questioning until she finally agreed to go over and see what the temperature was set at. Dr. Bob didn't seem to personally know where the thermostat was located. The former Ms. Shrew came back and said that somehow, the A/C had been mistakenly turned off and it wasn't her fault! She sternly suggested that Dr. Bob not interrupt her again.

At this point the group is beginning to covertly look at their immediate neighbors, then around the room, to see if anyone else might be thinking that this *Seminar* was beginning to go weird. I sense an undercurrent of desperation developing within the group, and since I'm in the middle of the front row, I turn in my little folding seminar chair and squarely face the four rows behind me, giving forth with a huge eye roll while shaking my head sadly. The former Ms. Shrew sees this and gives me a double death glare. I have the feeling I'm about to be sent to the Principal's office. Time passes apace.

The former Ms. Shrew then reluctantly surrendered the podium by asking Dr. Bob to do some explaining about the relationship between body winds and the digestive system with special emphasis to be placed on chronic constipation. He launches into several harrumphs and stares at the power point monitor with squinted eyes, indicating deep concentration, and begins: "Well, we THINK there might be SOME correlation between flatulence and chronic diarrhea." The group is thinking diarrhea? She just told us it was chronic constipation! What is it? Now the entire group is frowning and humming uneasily.

At this point she looks at him sternly and asks, "Dr. Bob, is your mike on?" He looks startled and starts messing with his little clip-on mike, which causes it to come loose and drop on the floor with an amplified *thunk*. She glares at him for a long moment and then reports to us that he just dropped his mike. He finally gets around to stooping over and retrieving his little mike and getting it loosely fastened to his tie. She then asks, "Is it on now?"

By now twenty long, hot minutes have gone by and we have no more information about the connection between flatulence and severe constipation, and/or diarrhea, than the parakeet in the reception room. By now the temperature in the room must be in the nineties and I'm beginning to slip into a coma. I innocently raise my hand and ask, "Is the air conditioner on yet?" There is a collective group humming and stirring at the thought that the A/C might still be off. She stares daggers all over my face and upper body. I studiously examine my shoelaces.

She attempts to change the subject of the cramped, overheated little room by saying, "We would like all of you to consider trying our specialized services if you have ever had body windage in your life, or even thought about having it. We think we have the cure and have been very effective in our treatment program so far." I timidly raise my hand again, which she plainly ignores. When Dr. Bob finally gives me a reluctant nod, I ask what percent of success they have enjoyed with their treatments so far. Dr. Bob responds that they have had "some success," but she overspeaks him by saying in a louder voice that they have had "excellent results."

She obviously wants to move beyond the question of treatment success and asks him, "Dr. Bob, wouldn't you agree that most windage is caused by excessive digestive juices, as well as perhaps chronic constipation and/or diarrhea?" Dr. Bob opines that "Yes, possibly most flatulence is caused by excessive digestive juices, especially perhaps chronic constipation and/or diarrhea, we think." He knows better than to question, or even hesitate, in his response to her.

Dr. Bob then says with a jocular tone that he would like to entertain us with some *exciting facts and figures* in a slide show, because why else would we have come to the seminar except to be entertained? Ms. Shrew chuckles grimly and stares hatefully at me because I have my hand waving around in the air again. I observe in a pleasant voice that the actual reason I came to the seminar was because my air conditioning was on the fritz again. This brings forth a large group laugh, and I shrug apologetically like it's not my fault the group finds humor in my sad confession.

Dr. Bob soldiers on, trying to get the group's attention back on the possible exciting facts and figures provided by the slide show with its pie charts and bar graphs. Just as he seems to find his focus, so to speak, the projector light flashes twice and then goes out. The smell of burned wiring hangs thick in the room. The former Ms. Shrew storms over to the projector, as if to intimidate it back to life. Both the dog and the pony have escaped the barn and are now running wild and free. I again turn back to the group and wiggle my eyebrows outrageously, as if to say, "Well, there goes the exciting facts, figures, and pie charts we were to be so well entertained with.

The projector will not be restored and the diagnosis is a burned-out bulb. She wants to know if Dr. Bob has a spare one, and he responds that he didn't even know the bulb was replaceable. Dr. Bob is decidedly low tech. Cripes, he didn't even know where the thermostat was!

Up to this point I had been studiously avoiding a glance at my watch because I didn't want to experience the heartbreak of knowing just how slowly time was passing. I had learned this trick as a child attending Sunday school. However, I finally did hazard a glance and was gladdened to discover that we had only another fifteen minutes to go before we were due to be released out of bondage. At this point I observed in a pleasantly surprised voice that it looked like we only had fifteen minutes to go and I was still wondering what caused my friends' chronic farting. I also wondered aloud whether my two friends experienced chronic bowel irregularity and excessive gastric juices. I then turned and asked if anyone in the group had troublesome bowels or excessive juices.

One homeless-looking wag in the back said that his bowels were okay but that he got the *toxic farts* if he *drank too much booze.* While not a very scientific cause for body winds, most people in the group agreed that this phenomenon also occurred to them from time to time.

The former Ms. Shrew tried once more to regain control of the group by saying, "Most of you nice people here tonight are women, except for two," which I believe was her not-so-subtle criticism of myself and my boozer friend in the back row. She went on to say that she wanted the women to know that sometimes the winds are caused by hormones, especially during pregnancy or during that *time of the month.* I innocently opined that men sometimes get *secondary windage* from overly hormonal women, especially during that *time of month.* Another lusty group laugh at this, especially from the boozer wag who whistled and said "right on" in an agreeable tone while offering me an *air high-five* from the back row. I suspect that he had endured a lively cocktail hour before coming to the seminar where he had been told there would be *refreshments.*

There seemed to be a heavy pause at this point which gave me the opportunity to stand up and say, "Well thank you for this very informative and valuable seminar on flatulence and severe constipation, and possibly chronic diarrhea. It certainly is a *hot topic,* so to speak, and I'll be sure to recommend your treatment program, whatever that might be, to my friends back in California." I further observed that I had developed a ferocious case of the winds within the past thirty minutes and was beginning to wonder about my own personal gastric juices. I then began making my way toward the door with everyone following behind, but not too close, shoving, sweating, grunting, and heaving like cattle leaving an overcrowded stock truck.

At this point in the group evacuation, a panicked Ms. Shrew was babbling on about there still being five minutes left in the seminar and that she was not quite finished. She said that she needed to get the women's contact information before they got away. Just the women's. She didn't seem to require my own personal contact information. I kindly offered to bring *those who had escaped* back in, but again she pointedly ignored me.

After several months of self-actualization therapy made necessary as a result of my emotional setback during the Flatulence-Constipation Seminar, I was finally able to feel better about myself and my shameless misbehavior. I promised myself that I would never do anything like that again.

And then, just yesterday … just yesterday I saw a notice in the local paper promoting a *Constipation, Chronic Diarrhea and Excessive Bodily Wind* Workshop. After calmly thinking through all the possible scenarios, I have decided it is my responsibility to attend this Workshop so that I might redeem myself as a seminar participant. Plus there has to be someone to provide a little comic relief if things start to go south again. That and the fact that my air conditioning is once more on the fritz and it's another hot day out there! However, this time I will sit in the back as near to the exit as possible. Just in case I get the body winds.

I wonder if they'll be encouraging questions?

EPILOGUE

My Very Complicated 16-Step Method for Writing a Simple Story

FOR ONE OF HER AP ENGLISH CLASS ASSIGNMENTS, my daughter, Savannah A. Kilbourne, the finest daughter in all the land, was instructed to write a piece on how to write a piece. She asked me how I go about writing a story. The following outline was my answer.

1) Begin by sitting around idly with nothing to do. Possess a blank mind, same as usual. Stare out window at squirrels. Idly wonder what they are thinking.

2) Slyly engage brain when it least expects to be asked to work. Then, gently sneak up on the creative process by remembering some random, exaggerated story that was once told to a good friend sometime in the past. Since the telling of many of these stories occurs while visiting the Sierra Nevada Taproom, consider doing that again. Memo to self: go to Sierra Nevada Taproom this day.

3) After the brain is beginning to think, sit down on window seat with legal pad and scribble out a rough structure of ideas and events for a possible story. Observe squirrel romance. Wonder where they live.

4) Next go to the desktop and type up most promising of the scribbled notes. Triple space to facilitate numerous corrections and additions, which may occur in next step if process is allowed to continue to gestate.

5)   That evening, just before vespers, take triple-spaced outline of possible story to Sierra Nevada Taproom. Go alone, by own self. Sit in usual *work* spot back by pizza oven. Order usual strong ale in personal mug. Fill in the triple-spaced notes with new and improved scribbling, while having second, less robust ale. Drive home the back way.

6)   When at home, seat self at computer. Attempt to decipher and process the scribbled notes made after two pints of nourishing ale while *creating* at Sierra Nevada Taproom.

7)   Next morning, not too early, listlessly mess around on the desktop for several hours while refining the latest edition of scribbled notes that have been turned into scribbled word processing the previous night.

8)   That afternoon, not too early, continue to polish up overall mess of words that aspires to be an entertaining story. Go through six or ten only slightly improved editions of the story. Sometimes change only one word. Sometimes change nothing. Do not go to Sierra Nevada Taproom this day. Stay home and work on story at computer.

9)   That evening show fourteen-year-old brainiac daughter the final scribbled version. Ask for her gentle opinion.

10) Make corrections that brainiac daughter has required. Most will have to do with improper use of "quotation marks," although sometimes she comments, "just starting the story over is your best option." That suggestion will have a direct effect on her dessert choices. Broccoli is healthier than chocolate. Methinks: "How sharper than a serpent's tooth

it is to have a thankless child" (King Lear, Act 1, Scene 4), or words to that effect.

11) In the morning. Mess around with the draft for several more hours. Use up a lot of perfectly good paper and ink. Ponder over recent brutal suggestion that story *just be started over.* Observe squirrels mating. Wonder why no baby squirrels are ever sighted. What can they be thinking?

12) That evening take latest edition back to Sierra Nevada Taproom for final *one ale review.* Go by self.

13) Next day. Show final draft to encouraging friend. The Sierra Nevada Taproom is an excellent venue for this *first public showing* of the story.

14) Have thankless *Serpent's Tooth* daughter check story one more time before final submission for publication.

15) Allow story to be published in *San Francisco Chronicle, Georgetown Times,* or *New Yorker Magazine,* whichever asks first.

16) In nurturing, friendly and creative environment, possibly Sierra Nevada Taproom, practice graciously accepting Pulitzer Prize for literature.

CPSIA information can be obtained at www.ICGtesting.com
Printed in the USA
LVOW082351210612

287098LV00003B/4/P